IN MATHEMATICAL
CIRCLES

IN MATHEMATICAL

CIRCLES

A SELECTION OF MATHEMATICAL
STORIES AND ANECDOTES

HOWARD W. EVES

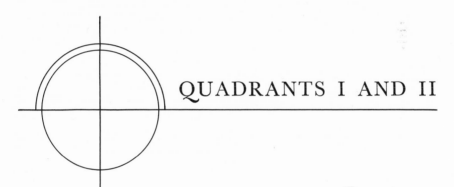

QUADRANTS I AND II

PRINDLE, WEBER & SCHMIDT, INC.

Boston ∘ London ∘ Sydney

FRONTISPIECE: Ancient mazes consisted of a tortuous path confined to a small area of ground and leading to a tree or shrine in the center, with no chance of taking a wrong turn. Shown in this volume is the circular maze constructed for the Minotaur. This labyrinth was delineated on the coins of Cnossus, specimens of which are not uncommon.

Library of Congress Catalog Card Number: 70-94459
SBN 87150-056-8
Printed in the United States of America

To the Mathematics Teachers of America
*with so many of whom I have
had the pleasure of working*

PREFACE

Somehow or other, over the years and without any particular effort on my part, a large number of stories and anecdotes about mathematics and mathematicians have fallen my way and remained stuck in my mind. These stories and anecdotes have proved very useful in the classroom—as little interest-rousing atoms, to add spice and a touch of entertainment, to introduce a human element, to inspire the student, to instill respect and admiration for the great creators, to yank back flagging interest, to forge some links of cultural history, or to underline some concept or idea. Many students and teachers have begged me to write up these stories and anecdotes, and a number of publishers have hounded me for them. At last I have given in and here offer a sample of the material.

Problems arose from the start. First of all, on marshalling the material I found I had far too much for a modest-sized venture; so I decided to select some three hundred to four hundred items as a test of reader interest. Next arose the problem of how to order the material; I decided to present it in rough chronological order with an accompanying index that would lend itself to other types of useful classification. And then there was the problem of the authenticity of some of the material; I decided not to make any effort at documentation, but simply to offer possibly doubtful items as part of the interesting accumulated folklore of our subject.

Undoubtedly many of the personal stories and anecdotes told here actually took place, but it is equally certain that some originally true stories have been embroidered over the years and ages, and that others have simply been made up as being apposite to the subjects concerned. Thus there are stories that have come down to us about some great men so lost in the mythical haze of the past that really nothing certain can be told about them; there are identical anecdotes that have been told about different persons; there are amusing tales that have circulated but have been denied by the principals involved; there are many cases where the same basic story has been told in varying and sometimes conflicting versions. One is reminded of Abraham Lincoln. There are literally hundreds of anecdotes that have been told about Lincoln; many of these have a real basis, but there can be no doubt that some of them were embroidered, twisted, or simply devised to fit the interesting and colorful character of Lincoln.

Particularly difficult is the matter of anecdotes about contemporary people. My collection contains a large number of such stories, but I have heard some of them denied or at least made much less interesting by the principals themselves. So, in this first round of stories, I shall stick to the past wherein the dramatis personae cannot rise up and defend themselves, and I shall refrain from narrating any anecdotes about the living.

The bulk of the material can be read with very little, and most often with no, mathematical background. But here and there do occur items a bit more demanding, and there are even a few challenging elementary problems. The historical comments and capsules are largely adapted from my book, *An Introduction to the History of Mathematics* (Holt, Rinehart and Winston, third edition, 1969). There the interested reader can find fuller historical treatments. I am very grateful to *The Mathematics Teacher*, one of the fine official journals of the National Council of Teachers of Mathematics, for permitting me to reproduce in essentially the original form certain items which appeared there in the Historically Speaking section, a department of the journal that for some years I have had the pleasure of editing.

It is hoped that the general reader may find the potpourri sufficiently savory, that the teacher may find it useful to serve on occasion, and that the partaking student may enjoy some of the historical tidbits and (in a noncannibalistic way) the human flavor.

With sufficient encouragement, I may decide to travel around the Mathematical Circle, or at least the more modern part of it, again in the future. Toward this possibility, interested readers are cordially invited to contribute any favorite stories they would like to see in an expanded collection.

HOWARD W. EVES

CONTENTS

CONTENTS

CONTENTS

Contents

QUADRANT TWO

Contents

Contents

Contents

QUADRANT ONE

*From a mathematical crow
to Hypatia's tragic death*

THE ANIMAL WORLD, REAL AND IMAGINARY

FAR, far back in time, before the appearance of Homo sapiens on the earth, there already were animals of various sizes and habits. Did any of these creatures possess even a tinge of mathematical sense? From the study, by competent observers, of present-day animal behavior, there has accumulated a weighty mass of evidence supporting the belief that certain birds and certain arthropods perhaps have such a quality. The conclusions are controversial and other plausible explanations have been offered. But many spiders do make beautifully symmetric webs of almost-perfect regular polygons, honey bees have long attracted admiration for the construction of their hexagonal comb-cells, some insects seem to possess an uncanny number sense when laying eggs, and most birds realize something is different when a sufficient number of eggs are added to or taken from their nests.

1° *A Scotch crow.* There is a touching and authentic story about a bird that seemed to possess a number sense. A squire in Scotland became annoyed by a raucous crow that had made its nest in the watchtower of his estate, and he determined to shoot the bird. Repeatedly he tried to enter the tower to blast the bird, but each time at the man's approach the crow would leave its nest and take up a watchful position in a distant tree. When the wearied squire would finally leave the tower, the bird would return to its nest. Not wishing to be outsmarted by a bird-brain, the squire resorted to a ruse. He secured the assistance of a neighbor one day. The two men entered the tower, one man came out and went away, and the other remained within. But the crow was not deceived; it stayed in the distant tree until the man within the tower came out. The experiment now became a contest, and the next day three men entered the tower, two came out and went away, and the third waited within to blast the pesky bird. But the crow was not fooled; it remained in the distant tree until the man within the tower came out. The next day the experiment was repeated with four men, but still without success. Finally five men entered the tower, four came out and went away, and the fifth remained inside. At this point the crow seemed to have lost count and,

3

unable to distinguish between four and five, it returned to its nest in the tower.

The conclusion of the story has not been recorded, but it is hoped that by the time of the final experiment a sufficient affection and respect had been built up for the crow so that the bird was allowed to remain nesting in the tower.

2° *The solitary wasp.* A striking instance of what may be number sense in insects is illustrated by the so-called *solitary wasp*. The mother wasp lays her eggs individually in separate cells and then provides each cell with a number of live caterpillars on which the young feed when they hatch. The remarkable thing is that the number of caterpillars is surprisingly uniform for a given species of wasp—some species provide five per cell, others twelve, and still others as many as twenty-four. Most surprising is the genus *eumenus*, a variety in which the female is much larger than the male. Somehow or other, the mother wasp knows whether the egg will produce a female or a male grub; if the egg is female she provides its cell with ten caterpillars, if the egg is male she provides its cell with five.

3° *The Harvard katydid.* The physicist, Professor George W. Pierce, of the Cruft Laboratory at Harvard University, has studied the songs of insects. There was a katydid in Dr. Pierce's laboratory that learned to count and thereby alter its usual two-beat rhythm. During an experiment, a laboratory assistant who could imitate the katydid's shrill "zeep-zeep," made the sound in three beats instead of two. The katydid answered with three beats. The assistant then tried four, and the katydid answered with four. Then the assistant tried five and the katydid answered with five. At the next stage, however, the insect lost count and, on its own, began to improvise on the numbers it had already learned.

4° *The ingenious honey bees.* Man has long shown interest in the seeming geometrical sagacity of the honey bees. The first known man to report on this mathematical acumen was the eminent Greek geometer Pappus, who flourished in Alexandria some sixteen hundred years ago. In Book V of his famous *Mathematical Collection* we find the following passage concerning the extremum properties of the cells of the bees' honeycombs:

> Presumably because they know themselves to be entrusted with the task of bringing from the gods to the accomplished portion of mankind a share of ambrosia in this form, they do not think it proper to pour it carelessly on ground or wood, or any other ugly or irregular material; but first collecting the sweets of the most beautiful flowers which grow upon the earth, they make from them for the reception of the honey, the vessels which we call honeycombs (with cells) all equal and similar, and contiguous to one another, and hexagonal in form. And that they have contrived this by virtue of a certain geometrical forethought, we may infer in this way. They would necessarily think that the figures must be such as to be contiguous to one another, that is to say, to have their sides in common in order that no foreign matter could enter into the interstices between them and so defile the purity of the produce. Now there are three rectilinear figures which are capable of fulfilling this condition, I mean regular figures which are equilateral and equiangular, for bees would have none of figures which are not uniform. . . . There being then three figures capable by themselves of exactly filling up the space about the same point, the bees by reason of their instinctive wisdom chose for their construction the figure which has most angles, because they conceived it would hold more honey than either of the other two.

5° *A classification of mathematicians.* Francis Bacon (1561–1626), the English moralist, prophet, philosopher, and man of letters, often engaged in scientific writings studded with aphorisms, many of which are particularly applicable to mathematics and mathematicians. For example, he divided philosophers into three groups—the ants, the spiders, and the bees. The ants are those who diligently but stupidly and unsystematically gather many little and generally useless bits of knowledge; the spiders are those who spin out intricate and insubstantial theories from their own minds; the bees are those who go to nature for raw material and inspiration, and through exacting labor transfer these into sound theories. These last he called the true philosophers. One can pretty well here replace "philosophers" with "mathematicians."

6° *Logarithms and multiplication.* When teaching logarithms in a trigonometry or algebra course, one can make a point and at the same time entertain the class with the following whimsical story.

One of our great national parks was yearly visited by a certain man. On one of these visits, the man met a snake and the snake's wife, but saw no little snakes. Accordingly, in conversation with the snakes, the man asked, "How come there are no little snakes?" "Well, you see," replied Mr. Snake, "we are adders, and cannot multiply." The following year, upon returning to the park, the man again found Mr. and Mrs. Snake, but now there were many little snakes. "How come there are so many little snakes?" the man asked. "Well, you see," replied Mr. Snake, "the park ranger came through here and built us a log table, so now we adders can multiply."

7° *Good induction versus bad induction.*   A scientist had two large jars before him on the laboratory table. The jar on his left contained a hundred fleas; the jar on his right was empty. The scientist carefully lifted a flea from the jar on the left, placed the flea on the table between the two jars, stepped back and in a loud voice said, "Jump." The flea jumped and was put in the jar on the right. A second flea was carefully lifted from the jar on the left and placed on the table between the two jars. Again the scientist stepped back and in a loud voice said, "Jump." The flea jumped and was put in the jar on the right. In the same manner, the scientist treated each of the hundred fleas in the jar on the left, and each flea jumped as ordered. The two jars were then interchanged and the experiment continued with a slight difference. This time the scientist carefully lifted a flea from the jar on the left, *yanked off its hind legs*, placed the flea on the table between the jars, stepped back and in a loud voice said, "Jump." The flea did not jump, and was put in the jar on the right. A second flea was carefully lifted from the jar on the left, its hind legs yanked off, and then placed on the table between the two jars. Again the scientist stepped back and in a loud voice said, "Jump." The flea did not jump, and was put in the jar on the right. In this manner, the scientist treated each of the hundred fleas in the jar on the left, and in no case did a flea jump when ordered. So the scientist recorded in his notebook the following induction: "A flea, if its hind legs are yanked off, cannot hear."

8° *The mathematical horse.*   There was a horse that showed a remarkable ability at learning mathematics. The horse mastered

6

arithmetic, and then elementary algebra. Soon after, it acquired plane and solid geometry, and next, trigonometry. Then it was offered analytic geometry, but upon this the horse balked, kicked, and carried on in a wild manner. All of which simply proves that one mustn't put Descartes before the horse.

PRIMITIVE MAN

THERE are stories gathered by explorers and anthropologists pointing up the meagerness of mathematical sense among very primitive peoples. It seems that the first mathematical considerations of man probably had their origin in simple observations stemming from human ability to recognize physical form and to compare shapes and sizes. This very early mathematics may be called *subconscious mathematics*.

9° *Two plus two.* Sir Francis Galton (1822–1911), English scientist, explorer, and anthropometrist, has related that the primitive Damaras of Africa, in bartering two sticks of tobacco for one sheep as the rate of exchange, became hopelessly confused when a white trader, desiring two sheep, offered four sticks of tobacco at once. Fraud was suspected by the Damaras, and the transaction had to be revised and carried out more slowly. First two sticks of tobacco were given and one sheep driven away, then two more sticks of tobacco and the second sheep claimed. When shown that the result came out the same as the trader's original proposal, the tribesmen regarded the trader as one possessed of magic powers.

Yet, these Damaras were not unintelligent. They knew precisely the size of a flock of sheep or a herd of oxen, and would miss an individual at once, because they knew the faces of all of the animals. To us, this form of intelligence, which is true and keen observation, would be infinitely more difficult to cultivate than that involved in counting.

10° *Addition of vectors.* Two vectors cannot be added by simply adding their magnitudes, inasmuch as the directions of the vectors are important in this consideration. An incredible story concerning the addition of vectors has been told by Martin Johnson, the famous world traveler. One day, in central Africa, Johnson came upon eight husky tribesmen on the verge of exhaustion as four pushed a mired Land Rover from the front and four pushed it from the rear without moving the vehicle an inch. The natives were much impressed with Johnson's ability to rearrange vectors when he placed all eight men behind the Land Rover and it moved forward quite easily.

11° *The great size of three.*   In the development, among primitive people, of vocal sounds to represent successively the first few small numbers, a sound is often finally reached which merely signifies "a great many." This, for example, is the case of those natives of Queensland who count "one, two, two and one, two twos, much," where the last term is meant to cover not only five, but all numbers larger than four. It is interesting that there are instances of the use of the very small number three in this sense of "much," or an excessively large number. For instance, the native Tasmanians count "one, two, plenty." Again, it is this use of three that we find in the Latin phrase "ter felix," which, though it literally means "thrice happy," is really meant to imply "very happy." It occurs again in the English "Thrice is he armed that hath his quarrel just," and in the French "très bien."

12° *Gog and Gug.*   There are a number of fanciful mathematical stories, of varying quality, about prehistoric or primitive people. Two of these people go by the names of Gog and Gug, and the following (which has appeared in several versions) is representative of the Gog and Gug stories.

In a certain tribe, in which polygamy was practiced, a married man's standing in the tribe depended upon the combined weight of his wives—the greater the combined weight, the more important was the man. Every year, on weighing day and according to custom, the married men would stand their wives on neatly spread animal skins, and the chief of the tribe would come around with a crude seesaw and balance the wives of one man against those of another in order to determine the relative importance of the men. Now Gog had only one wife, who was very heavy, while Gug had two much slenderer wives, and all year the two men argued as to who was the more important. When weighing day arrived, Gog placed his wife on a large hippopotamus skin, and Gug placed his wives on two small gazelle skins. When the weighing was performed, it was found that Gog's wife exactly balanced against the two wives of Gug. Thus it turned out that the two men were equally important, since, by the chief's ruling, "the squaw on the hippopotamus is equal to the sum of the squaws on the other two hides."

PRE-HELLENIC MATHEMATICS

IN the beginning, man considered only concrete mathematical problems, which presented themselves individually and with no observed interconnections. When human intelligence was able to extract from a concrete mathematical relationship a general abstract relationship containing the former as a particular case, mathematics became a science. This stage of mathematics may be called *empirical*, or *scientific*, *mathematics*, for mathematical findings were discovered by trial and error, experimentation, and other empirical or laboratory-type procedures.

There is no evidence that permits us to estimate the number of centuries that passed before man was able to raise mathematics from its subconscious stage to the scientific stage. As far back as history allows us to grope into the past, we find already present a sizeable body of scientific mathematics. There is historical evidence that this type of mathematics arose in certain river basins of the ancient Orient that cradled advanced forms of society. Among these river basins were the Nile in Egypt, the Tigris and Euphrates of Mesopotamia, the Indus and Ganges of south-central Asia, and the Hwang Ho and the Yangtze of eastern Asia. The deductive element is almost completely lacking in this early mathematics. It was not until the days of the Greeks, starting about 600 B.C., that deduction was made to play an essential role in mathematics, and mathematics became *systematic*, or *deductive*, *mathematics*.

The name of no mathematician of the pre-Greek period has come down to us, and so, of course, no personal mathematical anecdotes can be told for this era. Nevertheless, there are a number of interesting stories related to the mathematics of the period. Indeed, it would be difficult to find a more exciting mathematical story than that of Plimpton 322 (see Item 17°).

13° *Problem 79 of the Rhind papyrus.*   One of our chief primary sources concerning the mathematics of ancient Egypt is the Rhind, or Ahmes, papyrus, a mathematical text partaking of the nature of a practical handbook and consisting of eighty-five problems copied about 1650 B.C. in hieratic writing by the scribe Ahmes from an earlier work. The papyrus was purchased in Egypt by the English Egyptologist A. Henry Rhind and then later acquired by the British Museum.

Although little difficulty was encountered in deciphering and then interpreting most of the problems in the Rhind papyrus, there is one problem, Problem Number 79, for which the interpretation is not so certain. In this problem occurs the following curious set of data, here transcribed:

	Estate
Houses	7
Cats	49
Mice	343
Heads of wheat	2401
Hekat measures	16807
	19607

One easily recognizes the numbers as the first five powers of seven, along with their sum. Because of this it was at first thought that perhaps the writer was here introducing the symbolic terminology *houses*, *cats*, and so on, for *first power*, *second power*, and so on.

A more plausible and interesting explanation, however, was given by the historian Moritz Cantor in 1907. He saw in this problem an ancient forerunner of a problem that was popular in the Middle Ages, and which was given by Leonardo Fibonacci in 1202 in his *Liber abaci*. Among the many problems occurring in this work is the following: "There are seven old women on the road to Rome. Each woman has seven mules; each mule carries seven sacks; each sack contains seven loaves; with each loaf are seven knives; and each knife is in seven sheaths. Women, mules, sacks, loaves, knives, and sheaths, how many are there in all on the road to Rome?" As a later and more familiar version of the same problem we have the old English children's rhyme:

> As I was going to St. Ives
> I met a man with seven wives;
> Every wife had seven sacks;
> Every sack had seven cats;
> Every cat had seven kits.
> Kits, cats, sacks, and wives,
> How many were going to St. Ives?

According to Cantor's interpretation, the original problem in the Rhind papyrus might then be formulated somewhat as follows: "An estate consisted of seven houses; each house had seven cats; each cat ate seven mice; each mouse ate seven heads of wheat; and each head of wheat was capable of yielding seven hekat measures of grain. Houses, cats, mice, heads of wheat, and hekat measures of grain, how many of these in all were in the estate?"

Here, then, may be a problem that has been preserved as part of the puzzle lore of the world. It was apparently already old when Ahmes copied it, and older by close to three thousand years when Fibonacci incorporated a version of it in his *Liber abaci*. More than seven hundred and fifty years later we are reading another variant of it to our children. One cannot help wondering if a surprise twist such as occurs in the old English rhyme may also have occurred in the ancient Egyptian problem, though, in all likelihood, this twist was an Anglo-Saxon contribution.

There are many puzzle problems popping up every now and then in our present-day magazines that have medieval counterparts. How much further back some of them go is now almost impossible to determine.

14° *The pyramid of Gizeh.* The great pyramid of Gizeh was erected about 2900 B.C. and undoubtedly involved some mathematical and engineering problems. The structure covers thirteen acres and contains over two million stone blocks, averaging two and a half tons in weight, very carefully fitted together. These stone blocks were brought from sandstone quarries located on the other side of the Nile. Some chamber roofs are made of fifty-four-ton granite blocks, twenty-seven feet long and four feet thick, hauled from a quarry six hundred miles away, and set two hundred feet above ground. It is reported that the sides of the square base of the pyramid involve a relative error of less than one fourteen thousandth, and that the relative error in the right angles at the corners does not exceed one twenty-seven thousandth.

Of course, the engineering skill implied by these impressive statistics is considerably diminished when we realize that the task was accomplished by an army of 100,000 laborers working for a period of thirty years. For example, the seemingly difficult problem of raising the great stone blocks to ever higher positions as the structure of the pyramid grew was probably very simply met by constantly keeping the rising pyramid submerged in imported sand, hauling the blocks on rollers up a gradual incline of this sand, and then finally removing all the imported sand. Given sufficient time and sufficient labor power, many difficult feats can be done in a simple and primitive fashion. Nevertheless, the engineering problems had to be overcome one way or another. Consider, for instance, the mammoth engineering problems encountered by the Egyptians in quarrying and setting up some of their huge obelisks of pink granite. The largest existing obelisk appears before the old Temple of the Sun at Thebes; it was quarried about 1500 B.C. and is no less than 105 feet long, nearly 10 feet square at the base, and weighs about 430 tons!

15° *The greatest Egyptian pyramid.*   In the Moscow papyrus, an ancient Egyptian text dating from about 1850 B.C. and consisting of twenty-five mathematical problems, we find the following numerical example:

> If you are told: A truncated pyramid of 6 for the vertical height by 4 on the base by 2 on the top. You are to square this 4, result 16. You are to double 4, result 8. You are to square 2, result 4. You are to add the 16, the 8, and the 4, result 28. You are to take one third of 6, result 2. You are to take 28 twice, result 56. See, it is 56. You will find it right.

Now if we recall that the ancient Egyptians concerned themselves with only *square* pyramids, this certainly seems to be a numerical example illustrating the use of the formula

$$V = \tfrac{1}{3}h(a^2 + ab + b^2)$$

for computing the volume of a frustum of a square pyramid of height h and with bases of sides a and b. In the example, $h = 6$, $a = 4$, $b = 2$. The instructions of the problem carry us step by step through the substitution of these values for a, b, h in the above formula, resulting in the correct answer of 56 for the volume of the frustum. If this interpretation is the right one (and it is difficult to imagine that it is not), then we must concede to the ancient Egyptians the extraordinary achievement of the discovery of the formula. Now any rigorous derivation of the formula requires some form of the integral calculus, and so the discovery must have been an inductive, or empirical, one. No other unquestionably genuine example of this formula has been found in pre-Hellenic mathematics, and several involved conjectures have been furnished to explain how it might have been empirically discovered. It appears to be such a magnificent piece of induction that the historian of mathematics E. T. Bell has aptly referred to this early Egyptian example as "the greatest Egyptian pyramid," since the inductive discovery involved is perhaps more remarkable than the physical construction of any of the great stone pyramids of antiquity.

16° *Squaring the circle.* The earliest attempted solution that has come down to us of the problem of constructing a square equal in area to a given circle is found in the Rhind papyrus of about 1650 B.C. There we are told that the area of a circle is equal to that of the square having $\tfrac{8}{9}$ths of the diameter of the circle as a side. It is an elementary matter to show that this solution of the problem is equivalent to taking $\pi = (\tfrac{4}{3})^4$ or, approximately, 3.16.

One naturally wonders how the Egyptians arrived at the above approximate solution of the circle-squaring problem. In all likelihood, it was obtained by some sort of empirical procedure similar to the following: Draw a large circle on flat ground and cover its interior tightly with a large number of small pebbles, and only one pebble high, chosen as uniform in shape and size as possible. After this is done, convert the collection of pebbles from their circular array into a square array. On measuring the side of the square one will find it to be very close to $\frac{8}{9}$ths of the diameter of the original circle.

17° *Plimpton 322.* Archeologists working in Mesopotamia have systematically unearthed, since before the middle of the nineteenth century, some half-million inscribed clay tablets. Of these half-million tablets, about three hundred have so far been identified as strictly mathematical tablets containing mathematical tables and lists of mathematical problems. We owe most of our knowledge of ancient Babylonian mathematics to the scholarly deciphering and interpretation of many of these mathematical tablets.

Perhaps the most remarkable of the Babylonian mathematical tablets yet analyzed is that known as Plimpton 322, meaning that it is the item with catalogue number 322 in the G. A. Plimpton collection at Columbia University. The tablet is written in Old Babylonian script, which dates it somewhere from 1900 to 1600 B.C., and it was first described by Otto Neugebauer and A. J. Sachs in 1945.

Figure 1 gives an idea of the shape of the tablet. Unfortunately a

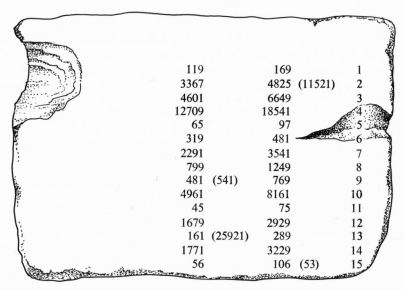

119		169		1
3367		4825	(11521)	2
4601		6649		3
12709		18541		4
65		97		5
319		481		6
2291		3541		7
799		1249		8
481	(541)	769		9
4961		8161		10
45		75		11
1679		2929		12
161	(25921)	289		13
1771		3229		14
56		106	(53)	15

FIGURE   1

I4

missing piece has been broken from the entire left edge and the tablet is further marred by a deep chip near the middle of the right edge and a flaked area in the top left corner. Upon examination, crystals of modern glue were found along the left broken edge of the tablet. This suggests that the tablet was probably complete when excavated, that it subsequently broke, that an attempt was made to glue the pieces back together, and that later the pieces again separated. Thus the missing piece of the tablet may still be in existence but, like a needle in a haystack, lost somewhere among the collections of these ancient tablets. As we shall shortly see, it would be very interesting if this missing piece should be found.

The tablet contains three essentially complete columns of figures which, for convenience, are reproduced on Figure 1 in our own decimal notation. There is a fourth and partly incomplete column of figures along the broken edge. We shall later reconstruct this column.

It is clear that the column on the extreme right merely serves to number the lines. The next two columns seem, at first glance, to be rather haphazard. With study, however, one discovers that corresponding numbers in these columns, with four unfortunate exceptions, constitute the hypotenuse and a leg of integral-sided right triangles. The four exceptions are noted in Figure 1 by placing the original readings in parentheses to the right of the corrected readings. The exception in the second line has received an involved explanation, but the other three exceptions can be easily accounted for. Thus, in the ninth line, 481 and 541 appear as (8, 1) and (9, 1) in the sexagesimal system. Clearly the occurrence of 9 instead of 8 could be a mere slip of the stylus when writing these numbers in cuneiform script. The number in line 13 is the square of the corrected value, and that in the last line is half of the corrected value, showing that the squares and the halves of certain numbers in the table probably played a role in the construction of the table.

Now a set of three positive integers, like (3, 4, 5), which can be the sides of a right triangle, is known as a *Pythagorean triple*. Again, if the triple contains no common factor other than unity, it is known as a *primitive Pythagorean triple*. Thus (3, 4, 5) is a primitive triple, whereas (6, 8, 10) is not. One of the achievements of the Arabians, two thousand years after the date of the Plimpton tablet, was to show that all primitive

15

Pythagorean triples (a, b, c) are given parametrically by

$$a = 2uv, \qquad b = u^2 - v^2, \qquad c = u^2 + v^2,$$

where u and v are relatively prime, of different parity, and $u > v$. Thus if $u = 2$ and $v = 1$, we obtain the primitive triple $a = 4$, $b = 3$, $c = 5$.

Suppose we compute the other leg a of the integral-sided right triangles determined by the given hypotenuse c and leg b on the Plimpton tablet. We find the following Pythagorean triples:

lines	a	b	c	u	v
1	120	119	169	12	5
2	3456	3367	4825	64	27
3	4800	4601	6649	75	32
4	13500	12709	18541	125	54
5	72	65	97	9	4
6	360	319	481	20	9
7	2700	2291	3541	54	25
8	960	799	1249	32	15
9	600	481	769	25	12
10	6480	4961	8161	81	40
11	60	45	75	2	1
12	2400	1679	2929	48	25
13	240	161	289	15	8
14	2700	1771	3229	50	27
15	90	56	106	9	5

It will be noticed that all of these triples, except the ones in lines 11 and 15, are primitive triples. For discussion we have also listed the values of the parameters u and v leading to these Pythagorean triples. The evidence seems good that the Babylonians of this remote period were acquainted with the general parametric representation of primitive Pythagorean triples as given above. This evidence is strengthened when we notice that u and v, and hence also a (since $a = 2uv$), are *regular* sexagesimal numbers—that is, are numbers of the form $2^p 3^q 5^r$ and thus have their reciprocals expressible as terminating sexagesimal fractions. It appears that the table on the tablet was constructed by deliberately choosing small regular numbers for the parameters u and v.

This choice of u and v must have been motivated by some subsequent process involving division, for regular numbers appear in tables of reciprocals and are useful in reducing division to multiplication. An examination of the fourth, and partially destroyed, column gives the answer. For this column is found to contain the values of $(c/a)^2$ for the different triangles. To carry out the division, the side a, and hence the numbers u and v, had to be regular.

It is worth examining the column of values for $(c/a)^2$ a little more deeply. This column, of course, is a table giving the square of the secant of the angle B opposite side b of the right triangle. Because side a is regular, sec B has a finite sexagesimal expansion. Moreover it turns out, with the particular choice of triangles as given, that the values of sec B form a surprisingly regular sequence which decreases by almost exactly $\frac{1}{60}$ as we pass from one line of the table to the next, and the corresponding angle decreases from 45° to 31°. We thus have a secant table for angles from 45° to 31°, formed by means of integral-sided right triangles, in which there is a uniform jump in the function rather than in the corresponding angle. All this is truly remarkable. It seems highly probable that there were companion tables giving similar information for angles ranging from 30° to 16° and from 15° to 1°.

The analysis of Plimpton 322 shows the careful examination to which some of the Babylonian mathematical tablets must be subjected. Formerly such a tablet might have been summarily dismissed as merely a business list or record.

18° *The angular degree.* We undoubtedly owe to the ancient Babylonians our present division of the circumference of a circle into 360 equal parts. Several explanations have been put forward to account for the choice of this number.

Thus it has been supposed that the early Babylonians reckoned a year as 360 days, and that this naturally led to the division of the circle into 360 equal parts, each part representing the daily amount of the supposed yearly revolution of the sun about the earth. Today this explanation is discredited, since we now have evidence that the Babylonians very early knew that the year possesses more than 360 days.

Again, the early Babylonians were very likely familiar with the geometric fact that the radius of a circle can be applied exactly six times to its circumference as a chord. Then, having adopted sexa-gesimal division, it was natural to divide the central angles of these chords into 60 equal parts, resulting in the division of the entire circle into 360 equal parts.

Otto Neugebauer, the great scholar and authority on early Babylonian mathematics and astronomy, has proposed an interesting alternative explanation. In early Sumerian times there existed a large distance unit, a sort of *Babylonian mile*, equal to about seven of our miles. Since the Babylonian mile was used for measuring longer distances, it was natural that it should also become a time unit, namely the time required to travel a Babylonian mile. Later, sometime in the first millennium B.C., when Babylonian astronomy reached the stage in which systematic records of celestial phenomena were kept, the Babylonian time-mile was adopted for measuring spans of time. Since a complete day was found to be equal to 12 time-miles, and one com-plete day is equivalent to one revolution of the sky, a complete circuit was divided into 12 equal parts. But, for convenience, the Babylonian mile had been subdivided into 30 equal parts. We thus arrive at $(12)(30) = 360$ equal parts in a complete circuit.

19° *Magic squares*. There are some Chinese mathematical works of which parts, at least, are claimed to date from very early times. This is difficult to verify because we lack original sources. As an added complication it was decreed, in 213 B.C. by the Emperor Shi Huang-ti, that all books in the country be burned and all scholars be buried. Although the edict was most certainly not completely carried out, and many books that were burned were soon restored from memory, we are now in doubt as to the genuineness of anything claimed to be older than the unfortunate date.

One of the oldest of the Chinese mathematical classics is the *I-king*, or *Book on Permutations*. In this appears a numbered diagram, known as the *lo-shu*, later pictured as in Figure 2.

The lo-shu is the oldest known example of a magic square, and myth claims that it was first seen by the Emperor Yu, in about 2200 B.C., as a decoration upon the back of a divine tortoise along a bank of the Yellow River. It is a square array of numerals indicated in Figure 2 by knots in strings, black knots for even numbers and white

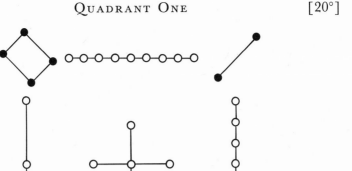

FIGURE 2

knots for odd numbers. The sum of the three numbers in any column is equal to the sum of the three numbers in any row, and also to the sum of the three numbers in either diagonal.

20° *The 3–4–5 triangle problem.* There are reports that ancient Egyptian surveyors laid out right angles by constructing 3–4–5 triangles with a rope divided into 12 equal parts by 11 knots. Since there is no documentary evidence to the effect that the Egyptians were aware of even a particular case of the Pythagorean theorem, the following purely academic problem arises: Show, without using the Pythagorean theorem, its converse, or any of its consequences, that the 3–4–5 triangle is a right triangle. The reader may care to try to solve this problem. Many different solutions have been given over the years. A particularly simple solution can be effected based on Figure 3, which shows four right triangles with legs of 3 and 4 units, along with a unit square, making up a square of 25 square units of area. This means that the hypotenuse of a right triangle with legs of 3 and 4 units is 5 units long, and it follows that a 3–4–5 triangle is a right triangle. This solution is found in the *Chou-pei Suan-king* (*The Arithmetical Classic of the*

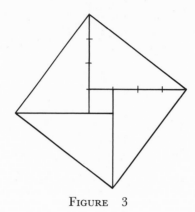

FIGURE   3

Gnomon and the Circular Paths of Heaven), a work generally regarded as the oldest of the ancient Chinese mathematical classics. The solution is easily generalized to obtain the Pythagorean relation for an arbitrary right triangle.

A FEW LATER CHINESE STORIES

THOUGH the following three stories of long-ago Chinese mathematicians postdate the Greek period, it seems convenient to place them here. The first story is a brief and sad biography; the other two are charming and semifanciful tales.

21° *The Drunken Dragon loses his hair.* The mathematician Ts'ai Yung, one of many Chinese calendric experts, flourished about 190 A.D. All of his works are lost to us. It has been reported that his persistent habit of conviviality earned him the name Drunken Dragon, and that at one time he was sentenced to death for political reasons, but at the last moment his sentence was commuted to having his hair pulled out.

22° *Huai-Wen calculates the dates on a tree.* Some of the early Chinese mathematicians became quite adept with the abacus and the calculating rods. There is a story that at the college at Chinyang, sometime around the year 560, a foreign Buddhist monk exclaimed over the calculating ability of the mathematician and metallurgist Huai-Wen.

Pointing to a jujube tree in the courtyard of the college, the monk asked Huai-Wen to calculate the number of dates on the tree. With the aid of his calculating device, Huai-Wen soon stated not only the total number of dates on the tree, but also how many were ripe, how many unripe, and how many only partly ripe. When, to test Huai-Wen's results, the dates were collected and counted, it was found that the mathematician was one date short. "It cannot be," said Huai-Wen, "shake the tree once more." And sure enough, one more date fell to the ground.

23° *I-Hsing finds his teacher.* The most famous of the Thang mathematicians was the monk I-Hsing, who flourished about 725 A.D., and who, by imperial order, once prepared a calendar. All of his books are lost. In the *Ming Huang Tsa Lu* of Cheng Chhu-Hui, written in 855, there is a brief account of I-Hsing's life.

It seems that before I-Hsing was introduced to the emperor, he had studied under Phu-Chu at Sung Shan. During an entertainment of monks there, a very learned member of the party, named Lu Hung, wrote an essay commemorating the meeting. In writing the essay, Lu Hung used very difficult words, and he announced that he would take as his pupil any student present who could read and understand the essay. I-Hsing stepped forward, glanced quickly through the essay, and then smilingly laid it down. Lu Hung was annoyed by I-Hsing's offhand manner, but when I-Hsing repeated the essay without a single mistake, Lu Hung was overcome and told Phu-Chu that this student was not one to be taught, but that he had better be allowed to travel.

So I-Hsing, wishing to study indeterminate analysis, traveled far and wide seeking an appropriate instructor. In time he came to the remote astronomical observatory at the Kuo Chhing Ssu temple, before which there was a courtyard with a spring flowing in it. As I-Hsing stood in the courtyard, he overheard an old monk inside the temple say, "Today someone will arrive to learn my mathematical art. Indeed, he should be at the door by now. Why doesn't someone bring him in?" Shortly the monk spoke aloud again, saying, "In the courtyard the waters of the spring are flowing westward--my student should be arriving." So I-Hsing entered the temple and knelt before the monk, who then and there began to teach the student his computing methods, whereupon the waters of the spring in the courtyard immediately turned and flowed eastward.

This story points up the difficulties of mathematical communication in those early days, and it shows how easily mathematical discoveries might die with the author.

THALES

ACCORDING to tradition, Greek mathematics appears to have started in an essential way with the work of Thales of Miletus in the first half of the sixth century B.C. This versatile genius, declared to be one of the "seven wise men" of antiquity, was a worthy founder of *systematic mathematics* and is the first known individual with whom the use of deductive methods in mathematics is associated. As with other great men, many charming anecdotes are told about Thales, which, if not true, are at least apposite.

24° *How to become rich.* One day, when still a poor man, Thales was conversing with an equally poor visiting friend. "The lot of a poor man is a hard one in this world," remarked the friend, "and if one is born poor one will remain poor the rest of his life." "Not necessarily so," replied Thales, "I am sure that if one should apply himself to the matter, it would be easy to become rich." "That is certainly easier said than done," rejoined the friend, "and I find it very difficult to believe." "I tell you what," said Thales, "when you visit me again six months from now, I will show you how easy it is to become rich." Six months later, when the visitor returned, he was astonished to find that his former poor friend was now the richest man for miles around, and he expressed his great surprise to Thales. "I merely wanted to show you how easy it is to become rich if you apply yourself to the problem," replied Thales. "Well, tell me, how did you do it?" asked the friend. "It was simple," explained Thales. "Foreseeing a heavy crop of olives coming, I went about and secretly bought up all the olive presses of the region. When it came time to press the oil from the olives, no one in the region had a press, and all had to come to me. I realized a fortune by renting out the presses. You see, it is easy to become rich if you but give the matter a little attention."

25° *The recalcitrant mule.* As one of his smaller business ventures, Thales had a salt mine up in the hills. Each day his mules came down the hill carrying bags of salt from the mine. The trail down the hill crossed a small stream, and one day while fording the stream one of the laden mules slipped and fell. In struggling to its feet, the mule chanced to roll onto its back and the salt dissolved from its bags, leaving the mule light and comfortable for the rest of the trip down the hill. The mule remembered this experience, and on the three successive days when it came down the hill it rolled about in the stream to dissolve and lose the contents of its load. Now ordinary mortals, like you and me, would have seized a stick and, with much shouting, would have beaten the animal over its hind quarters to cure it of this troublesome habit. But Thales was a "wise man," and the next time that mule came down the hill it was loaded with bags of sponges.

26° *Why Thales never married.* In his later and more affluent period of life, Thales was visited by his friend Solon, the great Greek lawgiver. As the two men sat discoursing one evening, Solon queried, "Here you are in possession of almost everything a man might desire— wealth and influence, health and comfort, fame and respect, knowledge and wisdom—but no wife. Tell me, my friend, why have you never married?" "That is quite a question," replied Thales, "and since the hour is so late, I believe I can better tell you in the morning." So the host and his guest retired for the night. In the morning they assembled for breakfast, but they had scarcely begun to eat their bowls of grapes when in raced a breathless runner with a message for Solon. Solon read the message and rose grief-stricken to his feet. "Thales," he hoarsely said, "I must leave at once for home. This message informs me that my favorite son has fallen from his horse and been killed." "There, there, my dear Solon," replied Thales soothingly, "please be seated and calm yourself. The message is a fictitious one, and I have contrived this whole event. I merely wanted to tell you why I never married."

27° *Thales as a stargazer.* One evening, while absently walking along and studying the stars, Thales inadvertently fell into a deep ditch from which he could not extricate himself. Finally his calls for help were answered by an old woman who managed to pull him from the ditch. When asked by the old woman what he had been doing to get himself into such a predicament, he explained that he had been looking at the stars, whereupon the old woman wondered, "How can you hope to see anything in the heavens when you can't even see what is at your own feet?"

28° *Credit where credit is due.*   When once asked what he would take for one of his discoveries, Thales replied, "I will be sufficiently rewarded if, when telling it to others, you will not claim the discovery as your own, but will say it was mine."

29° *Moral advice.*   When Thales was asked how we might lead more upright lives, he advised, "By refraining from doing what we blame in others."

30° *An incongruity.*   When asked what, in all his travels, was the strangest thing he had ever seen, Thales replied, "An aged tyrant."

31° *The Thales puzzle.*   It has been reported that Thales resided for a time in Egypt, and there evoked admiration by calculating the height of a pyramid by means of shadows. Two versions of the story have been given. The earlier account, furnished by Hieronymus, a pupil of Aristotle, says that Thales noted the length of the shadow of the pyramid at the moment when his own shadow was the same length as himself. The later version, given by Plutarch, says that Thales set up a stick and employed the fact that "the [height of the] pyramid was to the [length of the] stick as the shadow of the pyramid to the shadow of the stick." Both of these versions fail to mention the very real difficulty, in either case, of obtaining the length of the shadow of the pyramid (that is, the distance from the apex of the shadow to the center of the base of the pyramid).

The above unaccounted-for difficulty has given rise to what might be called the *Thales puzzle*: Devise a method, based on shadow observations and similar triangles and independent of latitude and specific time of day or year, for determining the height of a pyramid. Figure 4

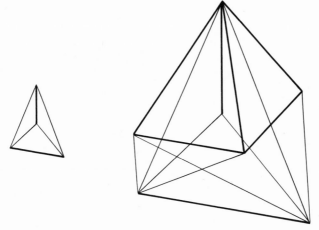

FIGURE 4

suggests a solution—that the reader may care to complete—requiring *two* shadow observations spaced a few hours apart.

32° *Thales, the engineer.* Thales was a resourceful man and has been credited with a now doubted spectacular feat in engineering. King Croesus, who was an admirer and probably one-time patron of Thales, had urgent need to transport his army across the river Halys. Boats were out of the question, pontoon bridges were still a thing of the future, and there was no time to build a permanent bridge. To resolve his predicament, Croesus consulted Thales. The wise man quickly saw a solution. He directed that a canal be excavated to divert the river into a temporary channel. After the army had passed dryshod over the former river bed, Thales had everything restored to its former order, so as not to offend the river gods that Croesus respected.

33° *Thales, the astronomer.* There is another story, also doubted today, that Thales predicted the total, or nearly total, eclipse of the sun that took place on May 28, 585 B.C. According to one version of the story, on that day the Medes and Lydians were locked in a battle during the sixth year of a stubborn war. The soldiers suddenly found themselves fighting in growing darkness. Terrified by the vanishing of the sun, the warring hosts quit the fight. A peace was concluded and later sealed by a double marriage between their respective reigning families.

A precise prediction of the time and locality of an eclipse of the sun requires a mathematical finesse far beyond what was possible in Thales' time. To have predicted just the year and the rough quarter of the globe of such an occurrence would have been a praiseworthy accomplishment in those days.

Also in connection with astronomy, it is said that Thales advised mariners to steer by the Little Bear rather than the Great Bear.

34° *Thales, the statesman.*   Among the many stories subsequently told of Thales by his admirers is that of his simple solution of the incessant brawling among the five Ionian city-states and of their openness as prey to outside invaders. The internecine warfare stopped and joint safety was secured when Thales suggested a federation of the city-states.

PYTHAGORAS

THE next man mentioned in the history of mathematics, after the illustrious Thales, is Pythagoras, who became enveloped by his followers in such a mythical haze that very little is known about him with any degree of certainty. After extensive traveling, he settled in the Greek seaport of Crotona, located in southern Italy. There he founded the famous Pythagorean School, which, in addition to being an academy for the study of philosophy, mathematics, and natural science, developed into a closely knit brotherhood with secret rites and observances. Many stories have come down to us about Pythagoras and his Brotherhood.

35° *The lure of geometry.*   It has been told that Pythagoras, in an effort to secure some students, found an impecunious young artisan and offered to teach him geometry. To make the lessons worth the poor pupil's time, the master agreed to pay him a penny for each geometrical theorem he mastered. This suited the young man well, for he found that by listening attentively he could earn better wages in an hour than in a full day at his usual labor. As his pile of pennies grew, the pupil discovered that in spite of himself he was becoming more interested in his studies than in his increasing wealth. Indeed, so avid did his interest in geometry become and so thoroughly did he fall under the subject's spell, that he begged his teacher to proceed faster, and as an inducement insisted that Pythagoras now accept from him a penny for each new theorem. By the time the pupil absorbed all the geometry he could hold, the gratified teacher had gained back all of his pennies.

36° *The first recorded facts in mathematical physics.* A remarkable discovery about numbers, claimed to have been made by Pythagoras, is the dependence of musical intervals upon simple numerical ratios. Thus Pythagoras is said to have found that for like strings under the same tension, the lengths should be 2 to 1 for the octave, 3 to 2 for the fifth, and 4 to 3 for the fourth. These results, apparently the first recorded facts in mathematical physics, are said to have led the Pythagoreans to initiate the scientific study of musical scales.

The manner of the above discovery by Pythagoras has been told repeatedly over the ages and runs as follows. While passing a blacksmith's shop one day, Pythagoras was arrested by the clang of four hammers swung in succession by four slaves pounding a piece of red-hot iron. All but one of the hammers clanged in harmony. Upon investigation, Pythagoras found that the differences in pitch of the four sounds were due to the different weights of the hammers. He persuaded the blacksmith to let him borrow the hammers for a short time. Taking the hammers home, he weighed them and then hung them individually to four strings of the same length and thickness. On plucking the strings, he noted that the emitted sounds corresponded to those made by the hammers striking the red-hot iron. By sticking a small lump of clay on the hammer responsible for the dissonance, he brought the emitted note for this hammer into harmony with the other three.

Now, curiously enough, there is a grave flaw in this often-repeated story, namely: *the tone of a hammer striking a given anvil is independent of the weight of the hammer.* A couple of minutes in a blacksmith's shop would have convinced any one of the erudite scholars who passed this legend on to their successors that the whole story is physically absurd.

37° *A hecatomb of oxen.* Legend has it that Pythagoras celebrated his discovery of the famous right-triangle theorem by sacrificing to the gods a hecatomb (that is, 100 head) of oxen. Concerning this sacrifice, C. L. Dodgson (Lewis Carroll), in his *A New Theory of Parallels* published in 1895, says:

> But neither thirty years, nor thirty centuries, affect the clearness, or the charm, of Geometrical truths. Such a theorem as "the square of the hypotenuse of a right-angled triangle is equal to the sum of the squares of the sides" is as dazzlingly beautiful now as it was in the day when Pythagoras first discovered it, and celebrated its advent, it is said, by sacrificing a hecatomb of oxen—a method of doing honor to Science that has always seemed to me *slightly* exaggerated and uncalled-for. One can imagine oneself, even in these degenerate days, marking the epoch of some brilliant scientific discovery by inviting a convivial friend or two, to join one in a beefsteak and a bottle of wine. But a *hecatomb* of oxen! It would produce a quite inconvenient supply of beef.

38° *A play on words.* In the German vernacular a dunce or blockhead is called an ox, or *Ochs*. Now after Pythagoras discovered his famous theorem he sacrificed a hecatomb of oxen. Since that time all *Ochsen* tremble whenever a new truth is discovered.

39° *A philosopher.* If the following sentiments, attributed to Pythagoras, are authentic, they furnish a fine summary of his life, character, and ideals.

"I have no trade," he once declared; "I am a philosopher."

"And what may that be?" he was asked.

"This life," he explained, "may be compared to the Olympic games. For in that concourse some seek glory or strive for wreaths; others, peddling goods, pursue profit; others again, less base than either, go to the games neither for applause nor for gain, but merely to enjoy the sport and keep abreast of the times.

"In the same way we men quitted our celestial home and came into this world, where many toil for honor and the majority for gain, and where but a few, despising greed and vanity, study nature for its own sake. These last I call philosophers."

40° *Friendship.* Asked what a friend is, Pythagoras replied, "Another I." From this developed the amicability of numbers. What could depict a closer friendship than the *amicable number pair* 220 and

284? The proper divisors* of 220 are 1, 2, 4, 5, 10, 11, 20, 22, 44, 55, 110, and the sum of these is 284; the proper divisors of 284 are 1, 2, 4, 71, 142, and the sum of these is 220. Each of the two numbers 220 and 284 generates the other; surely nothing can be more intimate than this.

41° *The marriage of Pythagoras.*   More than one teacher has married a young and admiring pupil. Pythagoras may have been the first to do this. According to the story, among Pythagoras's favorite pupils was Theano, the beautiful young daughter of his host Milo. Theano developed a hopeless infatuation for her teacher, who was so deeply submerged in his studies that he noticed nothing. So he was greatly surprised one day when Theano informed him that she was about to expire of an unreciprocated passion for someone. On persistent questioning by the master, Theano finally admitted that Pythagoras himself was the man she loved. To save her sanity, if not her life, Pythagoras sacrificed his asceticism and married her.

42° *Pythagorean teaching.*   Pythagoras taught his Brothers to refrain from wearing wool clothing (because of the transmigration of souls of men into animals), never to take a higher road if a lower one should be present (because of humility), and never to poke a fire with iron (because flame was the symbol of truth). More obscurely, he instructed the Brothers not to sit on a quart measure, not to touch a white rooster, and not to eat beans. He also taught the Brothers celebacy—in spite of his marriage to Theano.

43° *Pythagoras's golden thigh.*   The misanthropic philosopher Heraclitus has said that Pythagoras was the son of Mnesarchus, a stone cutter of Samos. And there is a vague rumor that Pythagoras's mother was of Phoenician extraction, and that she accompanied her son on one of his journeys. But to Pythagoras's disciples, the master was of divine origin, having for heavenly father none other than Apollo. In proof of this celestial descent, Pythagoras is said to have possessed a golden thigh. This curious legend is so persistent that it has been

---

* The *proper divisors* of a positive integer N are all the positive integral divisors of N except N itself. Note that 1 is a proper divisor of N. A somewhat antiquated synonym for proper divisor is *aliquot part*.

wondered if it might be a miracle-monger's distortion of some real physical infirmity, and, if so, what the infirmity might have been.

44° *The end of Pythagoras.*   In time the influence and aristocratic tendencies of the Pythagorean Brotherhood in Crotona became so great that the democratic forces of southern Italy destroyed the buildings of the school and caused the society to disperse. Pythagoras fled to Metapontum where he died, or was murdered, at an advanced age of 75 to 80. According to one legend, the master, fleeing from his pursuers, was forced into a bean field. Rather than chance treading on one of the sacred bean plants, Pythagoras chose death.

45° *Pythagoras's proof of his theorem.*   Tradition is unanimous in ascribing to Pythagoras the independent discovery of the theorem on the right triangle that now universally bears his name, that the square on the hypotenuse of a right triangle is equal to the sum of the squares on the two legs. We have seen, in Item 17°, that this theorem was known to the Babylonians of Hammurabi's time, more than a thousand years earlier, but the first general proof of the theorem may well have been given by Pythagoras. There has been much conjecture as to the proof Pythagoras might have offered, and it is generally felt that it probably was a dissection type of proof* like the following, illustrated in Figure 5. Let *a*, *b*, *c* denote the legs and hypotenuse of the

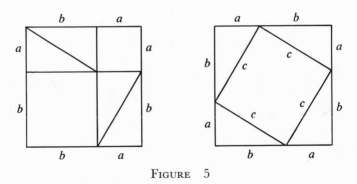

Figure   5

* See, however, Daniel Shanks, *Solved and Unsolved Problems in Number Theory*, Vol. 1 (Washington, D.C.: Spartan Books, 1962), pp. 124, 125.

given right triangle, and consider the two squares in the figure, each having $a + b$ as side. The first square is dissected into six pieces, namely the two squares on the legs and four right triangles congruent to the given triangle. The second square is dissected into five pieces, namely the square on the hypotenuse and again four right triangles congruent to the given triangle. By subtracting equals from equals, it now follows that the square on the hypotenuse is equal to the sum of the squares on the legs.

To prove that the central piece of the second dissection is actually a square of side c we need to employ the fact that the sum of the angles of a right triangle is equal to two right angles. But the Greek commentator Proclus attributes this theorem for the general triangle to the Pythagoreans. Since a proof of this theorem requires, in turn, a knowledge of some properties of parallels, the early Pythagoreans are also credited with the development of that theory.

THE PYTHAGOREAN BROTHERHOOD

46° *Motto of the Pythagorean Brotherhood.* The Pythagorean attitude of knowledge for its own sake, rather than for profit, is illustrated by the motto of the Brotherhood:

> A figure and a step onward;
> Not a figure and a florin.

47° *Himself said it.* The early Pythagoreans so revered the founder of their Brotherhood that it was considered impious for a member to claim any discovery for his own glory, but all must be referred back to the master himself. It is told that the Pythagorean Hippasus was justly drowned at sea in a shipwreck as punishment for irreverently claiming the discovery of the regular dodecahedron.

48° *Brotherhood loyalty.* A young and penniless member of the Pythagorean Brotherhood fell desperately ill while traveling in foreign lands and was taken to the nearest inn. There the charitable innkeeper nursed him, even though the young man made it clear that he had neither money nor goods with which to repay his host. When it became

Figure 6

certain that he was dying, the young man asked the innkeeper for a board on which to draw. With effort he managed to scrawl on the board the mystic pentagram symbol (see Figure 6) of his Brotherhood. Turning to the innkeeper, he said, "My good friend, hang this board outside your inn door. Some day a traveler who understands what I have drawn will pass this way and will stop and ask you about the sign. Tell him everything, and you will be rewarded." And just so did it happen.

49° *Damon and Phintias*.　There were two Syracusan youths of the fourth century B.C. who followed the Pythagorean mandate concerning friendship to such a degree that their names have become synonymous with the fine loyalty of that relationship. Phintias (sometimes incorrectly called Pythias) was sentenced by the tyrant Dionysius of Syracuse to die for treason. The condemned man begged a postponement of his sentence so that he might first return to his home in a neighboring village to arrange his affairs. His petition was granted provided he could obtain someone to remain in his cell as a pledge of his return. His friend Damon offered to do this, and expressed a willingness to die in Phintias's stead should Phintias not appear by the fixed time of the postponed execution. Unexpected predicaments delayed Phintias, and the scheduled day arrived. Damon, still fully believing in his friend's faithfulness, was led out for the execution. People gathered and began to express pity at Damon's credulity, when suddenly the delayed Phintias rushed breathlessly through the crowd into the arms of his friend. Each youth demanded to die for the other. Struck by this loyalty of friendship, Dionysius released both youths and expressed a desire to be admitted to their friendship.

50° *The three questions.* Every evening each member of the Pythagorean Brotherhood had to put three questions to himself: In what have I failed? What good have I done? What have I not done that I ought to have done?

PYTHAGOREANISM

51° *The transmigration of souls.* Pythagoras taught the transmigration of the individual soul from one body to another, even to that of a different species. Although bodies served as tombs or prisons of the soul, it was admitted that if a man led a sufficiently pure life his soul might be released from all flesh.

There is a Pythagorean legend that tells of a Brother (or perhaps Pythagoras himself) coming upon a citizen of Crotona beating his dog. The Brother charged the man to stop, declaring that in the dog's yowls of pain he recognized the cries of a departed friend pleading for mercy. "For the very sin you are committing," the Brother informed the citizen, "my friend is now this dog with you as his harsh master. At the next turn of the Wheel of Birth, he may be the master and you the dog. Pray that he will be more merciful to you than you are to him. It is only thus that he can hope to escape the Wheel." That the Pythagorean School was respected is evidenced by the fact that the legend claims the citizen immediately stopped beating the dog and begged the animal's forgiveness.

52° *Number rules the universe.* The Pythagoreans believed that the whole numbers were the elements of everything. Even such concepts as reason, justice, man, health, and marriage were identified with distinct whole numbers. Thus the whole numbers ruled the universe, and therefore one who should master the relationships of the whole numbers might be able to understand and perhaps even guide the affairs of the universe.

The lower whole numbers had the following special meanings.

One, as the originator of all numbers, was the most revered digit and was the number of reason. Two, the first even or female number, represented diversity of opinion. Three, the first true male number, represented harmony, being composed of unity and diversity. Four stood for justice or retribution, suggesting the squaring of accounts. Five, being the union of the first true male and female numbers, represented marriage. Six was the number of creation.

In their diligent effort to search out the relationships of the whole numbers, the Pythagoreans took the first steps in the development of number theory, and at the same time laid much of the basis of future number mysticism.

53° *Amicable numbers.*   Two whole numbers, it will be recalled from Item 40°, are *amicable* if each is the sum of the proper divisors of the other. For example, 284 and 220, which constitute a pair that has been ascribed to Pythagoras, are amicable. This particular pair of numbers attained a mystical aura, and superstition maintained that two talismans bearing these numbers would seal perfect friendship between the wearers; should one of the wearers, though separated from the other by half the circumference of the earth, receive even so small an injury as a pin prick, the other would be aware of it. The numbers came to play an important role in magic, sorcery, astrology, and the casting of horoscopes.

Curiously enough, it seems that no new pair of amicable numbers was discovered until the great French number theorist Pierre de Fermat in 1636 announced 17,296 and 18,416 as another pair. Two years later the French mathematician and philosopher René Descartes gave a third pair. The Swiss mathematician Leonard Euler undertook a systematic search for amicable numbers and, in 1747, gave a list of thirty pairs, which he later extended to more than sixty. A second curiosity in the history of these numbers was the late discovery, by the sixteen-year-old Italian boy Nicolo Paganini in 1866, of the overlooked and relatively small pair of amicable numbers, 1184 and 1210. Today more than nine hundred pairs of amicable numbers are known. These pairs are all of the same parity; that is, the two numbers of a pair are either both odd or both even. All the odd ones are multiples of 3; all the even pairs have the sum of their digits a multiple of 9.

A cyclic sequence of three or more numbers such that the sum of the proper divisors of each is equal to the next in the sequence is known as a *sociable chain* of numbers. Only two sociable chains are known. In 1918 the Frenchman P. Poulet found one of five "links":

12,496,   14,288,   15,472,   14,536,   14,264.

There is a twenty-eight-link chain starting with 14,316. A sociable chain of exactly three links has been called a *crowd*; no crowds have yet been found.

54° *Deficient, perfect, and abundant numbers.* Other numbers having mystical connections essential to numerological speculations, and sometimes ascribed to the Pythagoreans, are the *perfect, deficient,* and *abundant numbers*. A number is *perfect* if it is the sum of its proper divisors, *deficient* if it exceeds the sum of its proper divisors, and *abundant* if it is less than the sum of its proper divisors. So God created the world in six days, a perfect number, since $6 = 1 + 2 + 3$. On the other hand, as Alcuin (735–804) observed, the whole human race descended from the eight souls of Noah's ark, and this second creation was imperfect, for 8, being greater than $1 + 2 + 4$, is deficient. And thus we account for the many ills of our present world.

Until 1952 there were only twelve known perfect numbers, all of them even numbers, of which the first three are 6, 28, and 496. The last proposition of the ninth book of Euclid's *Elements* (ca. 300 B.C.) proves that *if $2^n - 1$ is a prime number, then $2^{n-1}(2^n - 1)$ is a perfect number*. The perfect numbers given by Euclid's formula are even numbers, and Euler has shown that every even perfect number must be of this form. The existence or nonexistence of odd perfect numbers is one of the celebrated unsolved problems in number theory. There certainly is no number of this type having less than thirty-six digits.

In 1952, with the aid of the SWAC digital computer, five more perfect numbers were discovered, corresponding to $n = 521, 607, 1279, 2203$, and 2281 in Euclid's formula. In 1957 the Swedish machine BESK found another, corresponding to $n = 3217$, and in 1961 an IBM 7090 found two more, for $n = 4253$ and 4423. There are no other perfect numbers for $n < 5000$.

The values $n = 9689, 9941, 11213, 19937$ also yield perfect numbers, bringing the list of known perfect numbers to 24. The perfect number corresponding to $n = 11,213$ was found in 1963 at the University of Illinois. This very large number consists of 6751 digits and has 22,425 divisors. The University of Illinois mathematics department has been so proud of the discovery of this large perfect number that its postage meter has been stamping on envelopes a rectangle bearing the statement, "$2^{11213} - 1$ is prime."

The pursuit of larger and larger perfect numbers shows how wrong was Peter Barlow who, in his *Theory of Numbers* of 1811, wrote about the ninth perfect number (corresponding to $n = 61$): "It is the greatest that will be discovered, for, as they are merely curious without being useful, it is not likely that any person will attempt to find one beyond it."

There are only twenty-one abundant numbers between 10 and 100, and these are all even. That all abundant numbers are not even follows from the easily established fact that $945 = 3^3 \cdot 5 \cdot 7$ is abundant. This is the first odd abundant number, and the only odd abundant number not exceeding 1000.

55° *Pythagorean philosophy and geometry at stake.* Pythagoras preached, with all the fervor of a Savonarola, that everything—simply everything—depends upon the whole numbers. Imagine the consternation, then, within the Pythagorean ranks when some Brother discovered the devastating fact that $\sqrt{2}$ is not a rational number, that is, cannot be expressed as the ratio of two whole numbers, and therefore appears to be independent of the whole numbers. The geometrical counterpart of this discovery was equally startling, for if $\sqrt{2}$ is not a rational number, it follows that a side and diagonal of a square possess no common unit of measure that can be stepped off exactly a whole number of times into each. This contradicted the firm intuitive belief that any two line segments must possess some common unit of measure, though perhaps very, very small. Now the entire Pythagorean theory of proportion and similar figures was built upon this seemingly obvious assumption. In one fell stroke, both the basic Pythagorean philosophy and much of Pythagorean accomplishment in geometry were threatened. It is reported that so great was the "logical scandal" that efforts were made for a while to keep the matter secret, and one legend has it that the first Pythagorean to divulge the secret to outsiders was banished from the Brotherhood and a tomb was erected for him as though he were dead.

56° *Pythagoras justified.* Every student of college mathematics learns of the remarkable mathematical accomplishment made toward the end of the nineteenth century wherein, by starting from a postulational development of the whole numbers (that is, positive integers) and making no further assumptions, one first obtains the set of all integers, then the set of all rational numbers, and then the set of all real numbers. Since the irrational numbers, like $\sqrt{2}$, are among the real numbers, we see that, at least so far as the real number system is concerned, the ancient Pythagorean belief that everything depends upon the whole numbers is today justified.

57° *The case for Pythagoreanism.* * Pythagoras said that number is everything, but, aside from his analysis of musical tones (see Item 36°), he did not make a strong case for his assertion. He could not be expected to do so, for science in his time was at a very primitive level.

An examination of a list of the key discoveries in physical science shows that a very strong case can be built for the Pythagorean concept that number rules the universe. Just consider Galileo's law of falling bodies, Kepler's laws of planetary motion, Newton's law of universal gravitation, Coulomb's law, Maxwell's electromagnetic wave equations, Prout's law of definite proportion and Dalton's law of multiple proportion in chemistry, Lisle's law of constant angles and Haüy's law of rational indices in crystallography, the Dulong–Petit law for the specific heats of solids, Faraday's law of electrolysis, the optical spectrum resulting from Fraunhofer's diffraction grating, Stefan's law of radiation, Planck's quanta, Mendeléeff's periodic chart of the chemical elements, Schroedinger's wave equation, and so on and on and on.

---

*Adapted from Daniel Shanks, *Solved and Unsolved Problems in Number Theory*, Vol. 1 (Washington, D.C.: Spartan Books, 1962), pp. 130–137.

PLATO

Plato, "the most winged, most charming, and best loved of all the philosophers of the Western World," was born in or near Athens in 427 B.C. He studied philosophy under Socrates there, and then set out upon his extensive wanderings for wisdom, studying mathematics under Theodorus of Cyrene on the African coast and becoming an intimate friend of the eminent Pythagorean Archytas. Upon his return to Athens around 387 B.C., he founded his famous Academy there, an institution for the systematic pursuit of philosophical and scientific inquiry. He presided over his Academy for the rest of his life, and died in Athens in 347 B.C. at the venerable age of eighty. Almost all the important mathematical work of the fourth century B.C. was done by friends or pupils of Plato, making his Academy the link between the mathematics of the earlier Pythagoreans and that of the long-lived school of mathematics at Alexandria. The Athenian school lasted some nine hundred years, until the Christians obtained from Emperor Justinian a decree that in 529 A.D. closed its doors forever.

58° *Plato's motto and the transfer of training.* Plato's influence on mathematics was not due to any mathematical discoveries he made, but rather to his enthusiastic conviction that the study of mathematics furnished the finest training field for the mind, and hence was essential in the cultivation of philosophers and those who should govern his ideal state. This belief explains the renowned motto over the door of his Academy:

> Let no one unversed in geometry enter here.

Thus, because of its logical element and the pure attitude of mind that he felt its study creates, mathematics seemed of utmost importance to Plato, and for this reason it occupied a valued place in the curriculum of the Academy.

In recent decades there has been vigorous controversy over the question of mental discipline and transfer of training, with contentions ranging from one extreme to the other. Thus there are those who, like Plato, claim that the study of mathematics develops the pupil's respect for truth and therefore results in honesty, that it develops neatness, power of concentration, and especially the power to think clearly. But the advent of a mechanistic psychology cast grave doubt upon the validity of such claims, and it was quite conclusively shown that transfer of training is not complete, automatic, and inevitable. There are many examples of dishonesty, lack of neatness, and failure to think clearly in nonmathematical situations on the part of students of mathematics, and many uncritical people have interpreted this to mean that transfer of training is nonexistent. Competent psychologists today seem agreed that the truth lies between the two extreme positions; transfer of training *can* take place *if* the subject is taught with this specific purpose in view.

59° *Michel Chasles and the forged autograph letters.* [The following true story, which is related to Item 58° above, is a mixture of the amusing, the pathetic, and the incredible. It is here told, with permission, in the words of Dean R. A. Rosenbaum, from his elegant narration in the Historically Speaking section of *The Mathematics Teacher*, May, 1959, pp. 365–366.]

Educators often consider the question of "transfer." For example, does the study of mathematics instill habits of logical thought which carry over to the analysis of problems in other rational disciplines? It is of interest in this connection to examine the behavior of professional mathematicians, to see whether they exhibit notably logical qualities in the nonmathematical aspects of their lives. The spectacle of a mathematician acting in a markedly irrational manner fills most observers with unholy glee. No such spectacle can surpass that of Michel Chasles and the forged autograph letters.

Chasles was one of the foremost geometers of the nineteenth century. His *Aperçu historique sur l'origine et le développement des méthodes en Géométrie . . .*, published as a memoir of the Academy of Brussels in 1837, is an extraordinary achievement of synthesis and generalization which won him immediate recognition. He contributed many theorems to geometry, and the "principle of algebraic correspondence" is known by his name. Joseph Bertrand quotes what he refers to as an oft-repeated sentence, "All the geometers of Europe are disciples of M. Chasles."

But Chasles was an especially ardent French patriot, and his

nationalistic pride led to a debacle. When shown some letters, pur-
portedly written by Pascal, in which the laws of gravitational attraction
were set out, he eagerly bought them; here was proof of France's
priority to Newton's England! A scholar and bibliophile with a
comfortable income, Chasles continued to buy documents from one
Vrain-Denis Lucas during the period 1861–69.

The details of his purchases seem incredible. He bought over
27,000 letters, for about 140,000 francs. There were 175 letters from
Pascal to Newton, 139 from Pascal to Galileo, and large numbers
written by Galileo. But Lucas provided ancient, nonmathematical
letters as well. Included in Chasles' purchases were six from Alexander
the Great to Aristotle, one from Cleopatra to Caesar, one from Mary
Magdalene to Lazarus, and one from Lazarus to St. Peter. Every
letter was written on paper, and in French! It is probably true that
Chasles, in his ardor and enthusiasm, did not look at many of his
27,000 purchases.

When Chasles disclosed to the French Academy of Sciences his
theory of Pascal's priority to Newton, there was considerable scepticism.
Chasles displayed some of his letters, and it was pointed out that the
handwriting was not the same as that of letters which were indubitably
Pascal's. Various anachronisms appeared. Each was met by a new
letter furnished by Lucas, in which the difficulties were explained away.
But after several years of controversy, Chasles had to acknowledge
defeat. He exhibited his entire stock of 27,000 forged letters, and Lucas
was sent to prison for two years.

Lucas's defense at his trial was interesting. He maintained that he
had done nothing wrong—that Chasles had really received his money's
worth, that the controversy and trial, which were widely reported, had
stimulated in the public a healthy interest in history, that the debates
in the Academy had been much more exciting than usual, and that he,
himself, had acted through patriotic motives.

At the same time that one marvels at Chasles' gullibility, one
must be amazed by Lucas's industry: to "antique" paper for 27,000
letters is itself quite a task! Lucas apparently had spent many hours
each day in libraries, acquiring historical knowledge for his writings.
Since he knew neither Greek nor Latin, he was severely handicapped
in his work. According to J. A. Farrer (in his *Literary Forgeries*, Long-

mans, Green, and Co., 1907, Chap. xii), nothing is known of Lucas after his prison sentence; but Bertrand reports that Lucas served his time, returned to his "profession" after release, and was resentenced to three years as a recidivist, Chasles asking wryly, "Wouldn't it have been better to sentence him to five years from the start?"

Apparently Chasles was greatly embarrassed by the affair, and Bertrand remarks that the man had suffered enough—the matter should be forgotten. But Farrer can't resist giving a twist of the knife, which may well serve as a warning to all of us:

> The logical incapacity that M. Chasles displayed throughout the contest subsequently waged over his supposed treasures shows conclusively how insignificant is the benefit conferred on the reasoning faculties by mathematical studies. The leading mathematician of his country showed himself incapable of reasoning better than a child.

60° *Some particularly elusive Platonic numerology.* Plato was much influenced by the early Pythagoreans and it would seem that, at heart, he was a numerologist so far as his own mathematical beliefs went. There is no profundity in all of his works that has given his commentators more trouble than the following passage from Book VIII of his *Republic*:

> For that which, though created, is divine, a recurring period exists, which is embraced by a perfect number. For that which is human, however, by that one for which it first occurs that the increasings of the dominant and the dominated, when they take three spaces and four boundaries making similar and dissimilar and increasing and decreasing, cause all to appear familiar and expressible.
>
> Whose base, modified, as four to three, then married to five, three times increased, yields two harmonies: one equal multiplied by equal, a hundred times the same: the other equal in length to the former, but oblong, a hundred of the numbers upon expressible diameters of five, each diminished by one, or by two if inexpressible, and a hundred cubes of three. This sum now, a geometrical number, is lord over all these affairs, over better and worse births; and when in ignorance of them, the guardians unite the brides and bridegrooms wrongly, the children will not be well-endowed, either in their constitutions or in their fates.

The reader may care to try to unravel the mathematical basis of this strange and oracular passage. The passage defied analysis even by

Plato's immediate successors, and it was not until some 2300 years later that a satisfactory explanation was given. The elucidation appeared in a fascinating article in the *Proceedings of the London Mathematical Society* of 1925, and was given by Grace Chisholm Young, an eminent British mathematician of the early twentieth century. One must read Mrs. Young's article to appreciate her penetrating analysis, but one remarkable conclusion reached by Mrs. Young is that Plato guessed, and possibly proved, that *the only relatively prime whole numbers x, y, z, w simultaneously satisfying*

$$x^2 + y^2 = z^2 \quad and \quad x^3 + y^3 + z^3 = w^3,$$

are $x = 3, y = 4, z = 5, w = 6$.

61° *The five Platonic solids.* A polyhedron is said to be *regular* if its faces are congruent regular polygons and its polyhedral angles are all congruent. While there are regular polygons of all orders, it is surprising that there are only five different regular polyhedra. The regular polyhedra are named according to the number of faces each possesses. Thus there is the tetrahedron with 4 triangular faces, the hexahedron (or cube) with 6 square faces, the octahedron with 8 triangular faces, the dodecahedron with 12 pentagonal faces, and the icosahedron with 20 triangular faces. See Figure 7.

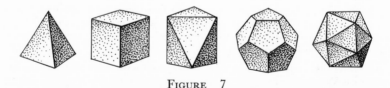

FIGURE 7

The early history of these regular polyhedra is lost in the dimness of the past. A mathematical treatment of them is initiated in Book XIII of Euclid's *Elements*. The first scholium (in all likelihood added later and probably taken from Geminus) of this book remarks that the book "will treat of the so-called Platonic solids, incorrectly named, because three of them, the tetrahedron, cube, and dodecahedron are due to the Pythagoreans, while the octahedron and icosahedron are due to Theaetetus." This could well be the case.

In any event, a description of all five regular polyhedra was given by Plato, who, in his *Timaeus*, shows how to construct models of the solids by putting triangles, squares, and pentagons together to form their faces. Plato's Timaeus is the Pythagorean Timaeus of Locri, whom Plato presumably met when he visited Italy. In Plato's work, Timaeus mystically associates the four easily constructed solids—the tetrahedron, octahedron, icosahedron, and cube—with the four Empedoclean primal "elements" of all material bodies—fire, air, water, and earth. The disturbing difficulty of accounting for the fifth solid, the dodecahedron, is taken care of by associating it with the enveloping universe.

62° *Kepler's explanation of the Timaeus associations.* Johannes Kepler, master astronomer, mathematician, and numerologist of later times (1571–1630), gave an ingenious explanation of the Timaeus associations of the five Platonic solids. Of the regular solids, he intuitively assumed that the tetrahedron encloses the smallest volume for its surface, while the icosahedron encloses the largest. Now these volume–surface relations are qualities of dryness and wetness, respectively, and since fire is the driest of the four "elements" and water the wettest, the tetrahedron must represent fire and the icosahedron water. The cube is associated with earth since the cube, resting foursquarely on one of its square faces, has the greatest stability. On the other hand, the octahedron, held lightly by two of its opposite vertices between a forefinger and thumb, easily spins and has the instability of air. Finally, the dodecahedron is associated with the universe because the dodecahedron has twelve faces and the zodiac has twelve signs.

63° *The Platonic solids in nature.* The tetrahedron, cube, and octahedron can be found in nature as crystals, for example as crystals of sodium sulphantimoniate, common salt, and chrome alum, respectively. The other two cannot occur in crystal form, but have been observed as skeletons of microscopic sea animals called *radiolaria*.

64° *The most extraordinary application of the Platonic solids to a scientific problem.* Kepler's mystical awe of the five Platonic solids extended beyond the association of these solids with the four primal "elements" and the enveloping universe. According to Kepler, these five solids accounted for both the number of planets (only five were known in his day) and the way the planets are spaced about the sun. In his *Mysterium cosmographicum* of 1596, Kepler says:

> The orbit of the Earth is a circle: round the sphere to which this circle belongs, describe a dodecahedron; the sphere including this will give the orbit of Mars. Round Mars describe a tetrahedron; the circle including this will be the orbit of Jupiter. Describe a cube round Jupiter's orbit; the circle including this will be the orbit of Saturn. Now inscribe in the Earth's orbit an icosahedron; the circle inscribed in it will be the orbit of Venus. Inscribe an octahedron in the orbit of Venus; the circle inscribed in it will be Mercury's orbit. This is the reason of the number of the planets.

We see that Johannes Kepler was a confirmed Pythagorean. He even once suggested the possibility that the soul of Pythagoras may have taken up residence in his body.

65° *Some problems concerning the Platonic solids.*

(1) In Item 61°, the definition of regularity of a polyhedron involves three properties: regular faces, congruent faces, congruent polyhedral angles. Many textbooks on solid geometry do not give all three of the defining properties. The interested reader may care to show, by counterexamples, that all three properties are necessary.

(2) From the three defining properties listed in (1), one can deduce the regularity of the polyhedral angles. The reader is invited to do this, and then to show that the three defining properties can be replaced by only two: regular faces and regular polyhedral angles.

(3) The uninitiated will almost always intuitively believe that of the regular dodecahedron (a solid having 12 faces) and a regular icosahedron (a solid having 20 faces) inscribed in the same sphere, the icosahedron has the greater volume. The reader is invited to show that the reverse is actually the case, and also to show that of a cube (a solid having 6 faces) and a regular octahedron (a solid having 8 faces) inscribed in the same sphere, the cube has the larger volume.

(4) It is interesting that a regular dodecahedron and a regular icosahedron inscribed in the same sphere have a common inscribed

sphere. Prove this, and show that the same is true of a cube and a regular octahedron inscribed in the same sphere.

(5) In Item 62° we noted that Kepler intuitively assumed that, of the five regular solids, for a given surface area the tetrahedron encloses the smallest volume and the icosahedron encloses the largest volume. Is this so?

(6) A regular dodecahedron, a regular icosahedron, and a cube are inscribed in the same sphere. Prove that the volume of the dodecahedron is to the volume of the icosahedron as the length of an edge of the cube is to the length of an edge of the icosahedron.

(7) In the so-called Book XIV of Euclid's *Elements*, it is pointed out that Hypsicles observed that if a regular dodecahedron and a regular icosahedron are inscribed in the same sphere, then their volumes are in the same ratio as their surface areas. Prove this.

(8) Show that the circumcircles of the faces of the regular dodecahedron and the regular icosahedron inscribed in the same sphere are equal.

66° *The Delian problem.*   Plato was born in, or close to, the year of the plague that killed a large portion of the population of Athens. The great impression that this catastrophe made may be the origin of a famous mathematical problem of Greek antiquity.* There is a report that a delegation was sent to the oracle of Apollo on the island of Delos to inquire how the plague might be averted. The oracle replied that the cubical altar to Apollo must be doubled in size. The Athenians accordingly doubled the dimensions of the altar, but the plague did not subside. Returning to the oracle for an explanation of the failure, the Athenians were informed that they had not carried out the orders; they had not *doubled* the size of the altar, but had increased it to *eight times* its original size. Thus arose the geometry problem: to find the edge of a cube whose volume shall be exactly twice the volume of a given cube. The problem remained refractory and in time was reputedly taken to Plato, who submitted it to the geometers. It is this story that has led the problem of duplicating a cube frequently to be referred to as the *Delian problem*. Whether the story is true or not, the problem was

---

* For a more likely origin of the problem, see Item 246°.

studied in Plato's Academy, and there are higher geometry solutions attributed to Eudoxus, to Menaechmus, and even (though probably erroneously) to Plato himself.

EUCLID

DISAPPOINTINGLY little is known about the life and personality of Euclid except that he was the first professor of mathematics at the famed Museum of Alexandria (which opened its doors about 300 B.C.), and apparently the founder of the illustrious and long-lived Alexandrian School of Mathematics. Even his dates and his birthplace are not known, but it seems probable that he received his mathematical training in the Platonic school at Athens. Although he was the author of at least ten works, and fairly complete texts of five of these have come down to us, his reputation rests mainly on his *Elements*. As soon as this work appeared it was accorded the highest respect. No work, except the Bible, has been more widely used, edited, or studied, and probably no work has exercised greater influence on scientific thinking.

67° *The royal road in geometry.* Only two anecdotes about Euclid have come down to us, and both are doubtful. In his *Eudemian Summary*, Proclus (410–485) tells us that Ptolemy Soter, the first King of Egypt and the founder of the Alexandrian Museum, patronized the Museum by studying geometry there under Euclid. He found the subject difficult and one day asked his teacher if there weren't some easier way to learn the material. To this Euclid replied, "Oh King, in the real world there are two kinds of roads, roads for the common people to travel upon and roads reserved for the King to travel upon. In geometry there is no royal road."

This is an example of an anecdote told also in relation to other people, for Stobaeus has narrated it in connection with Menaechmus when serving as instructor to Alexander the Great.

Since so many students are considerably more able as algebraists than as geometers, analytic geometry, which studies geometry with the aid of algebra, has been described as the "royal road in geometry" that Euclid thought did not exist.

68° *Euclid and the student.* The second anecdote about Euclid that has come down to us is an unreliable but pretty story told by Stobaeus in his collection of extracts, sayings, and precepts for his son. One of Euclid's students, when he had learned the first proposition, asked his teacher, "But what is the good of this and what shall I get by learning these things?" Thereupon Euclid called a slave and said, "Give this fellow a penny, since he must make gain from what he learns."

69° *Euclid's* Elements *compared with Newton's* Principia. Augustus De Morgan (1806–1871) once asserted: "The thirteen books of Euclid must have been a tremendous advance, probably even greater than that contained in the *Principia* of Newton."

70° *The most famous single utterance in the history of science. The utterance:* If a straight line falling on two straight lines makes the interior angles on the same side together less than two right angles, the two straight lines, if produced indefinitely, meet on that side on which the angles are together less than two right angles.

What is it? It is the *fifth,* or so-called *parallel, postulate* of Euclid's *Elements.*

Why is it famous? The lack of terseness and ready comprehensibility of this postulate, when compared with Euclid's other postulates, proved to be the source of much controversy. The dissatisfaction of mathematical scholars with its statement as a postulate is indicated by the fact that many geometers attempted over a period of some twenty centuries either to derive it from Euclid's other postulates and axioms or to replace it by a more acceptable equivalent. This concern over Euclid's fifth postulate furnished the stimulus for the development of a great deal of modern mathematics, and also led to deep and revealing inquiries into the logical and philosophical foundations of the subject. In particular, it led to the liberation of geometry from its traditional mold and to the subsequent creation of many other equally consistent geometries different from that of Euclid. Indeed, it had a similar liberating effect on mathematics as a whole. It dealt a severe blow to the *absolute truth* viewpoint of mathematics and brought forth a new view of the nature of a postulate. Mathematics emerged as an arbitrary creation of the human mind, not as something essentially dictated to us of necessity by the world in which we live.

Who named it so? Cassius J. Keyser, in his *Mathematical Philosophy* (New York: E. P. Dutton and Company, Inc., 1922), p. 113.

71° *The most fruitful single utterance in the history of science.* The question, "Why?"

ARCHIMEDES

ONE of the very greatest mathematicians of all time, and certainly the greatest of antiquity, was Archimedes, a native of the Greek city of Syracuse on the island of Sicily. He was born about 287 B.C. and died during the Roman pillage of Syracuse in 212 B.C. As a youth he studied mathematics at the Museum of Alexandria under the successors of Euclid, after which he returned to his native city to produce his mathematical masterpieces. Some ten treatises by Archimedes have come down to us and there are various traces of lost works. Probably the most remarkable contribution made to mathematics in these works is the early development of some of the methods of the integral calculus.

72° *Archimedes' boast.* It is narrated by Plutarch (ca. A.D. 46–120), in his *Life of Marcellus*, that Archimedes once boasted that if he had a place to stand on he could move the earth. King Hiero of Syracuse was struck with amazement at this statement and asked Archimedes to make good his boast by actually moving some enormous weight. Accordingly a ship, which could not be drawn out of dry dock without the combined labor of a large contingent of men, was loaded with many passengers and a full freight, and Archimedes was asked to move the ship into the water. Seated comfortably in a chair on the beach, the great mathematician and physicist astonished the King and the spectators by effortlessly and singlehandedly causing the ship, by means of a compound pulley arrangement, to slip easily into the sea.

73° *Archimedes' defense of Syracuse.* Impressed with Archimedes' easy success in singlehandedly moving a loaded ship from dry dock to the sea, King Hiero prevailed upon Archimedes to assist in the defense of Syracuse when that city was under the siege directed by the Roman general Marcellus. Many stories have been told of the ingenious contrivances devised by Archimedes to aid his city. There were catapults with adjustable ranges capable of hurling huge projectiles through loopholes in protective bastions. There were movable projecting poles for dropping heavy weights on enemy ships that approached too near the city walls. There were great grappling cranes that hoisted enemy ships from the water and violently shook them till the terrified sailors fell overboard and the ships began to crack up. A story that Archimedes used large burning-glasses to set the enemy's vessels afire is of later origin, but could be true. It has been said that Archimedes had the foes so confounded and frightened that all he had to do was to hang a free end of rope over the city's wall, and the Romans, fearing some horrible contrivance was on the other end, were afraid to go near it. Because of Archimedes' defensive machines, Syracuse held out against the Roman siege and blockade for close to three years. The city's defenses were finally broken only when, during a celebration, the Syracusans overconfidently relaxed their watches.

74° *The fraudulent goldsmith.* Apparently Archimedes was capable of strong mental concentration, and tales are told of his obliviousness to surroundings when engrossed by a problem. Typical is the frequently told story of King Hiero's crown and the suspected goldsmith.

It seems that King Hiero, desiring a crown of gold, gave a certain weight of the metal to a goldsmith, along with instructions. In due time the crown was completed and given to the king. Though the crown was of the proper weight, for some reason the king suspected that the goldsmith had pocketed some of the precious metal and replaced it with silver. The king didn't want to break the crown open to discover if it contained any hidden silver, and so in his perplexity he referred the matter to Archimedes. For a while, even Archimedes was puzzled. Then, one day when in the public baths, Archimedes hit upon the solution by discovering the first law of hydrostatics. In his flush of excitement, forgetting to clothe himself, he rose from his bath and ran home through the streets shouting, "Eureka, eureka" ("I have found it, I have found it").

The famous first law of hydrostatics appeared later as Proposition 7 of the first book of Archimedes' work *On Floating Bodies*. This law, which today every student of physics learns in high school, says that "a body immersed in a fluid is buoyed up by a force equal to the weight of the displaced fluid." This means that of two equal masses of different materials, that one having the greater volume will lose more when the two masses are weighed under water. Thus, since silver is more bulky than gold, it suffers a greater change when weighed under water than does an equal mass of gold. So all Archimedes had to do was to put the crown on one pan of a balance and an equal weight of gold on the other pan, and then immerse the whole in water. In this situation the gold would outweigh the crown if the latter contained any hidden silver. Tradition says that the pan containing the crown rose, and in this way the goldsmith was shown to be dishonest.

75° *The Archimedean screw.* One of Archimedes' inventions, still used in various parts of the world, is the so-called *Archimedean screw*. It consists of a tube (see Figure 8), open at each end, wrapped in

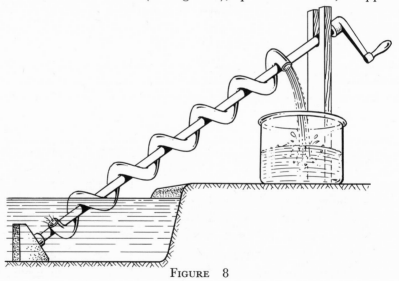

FIGURE   8

helical or cork-screw fashion around a central cylindrical core. One end of the screw is immersed in water and the axis of the screw is inclined to the vertical at a sufficiently large angle. The instrument is then turned, by a handle at its upper end, around its axis. If the inclination of the axis of the screw to the vertical is greater than the pitch of the screw, water will flow along the tube and out the upper end. The Archimedean screw was used in Egypt for irrigating fields and for draining inundated areas. It was also frequently used to empty water from holds of ships.

76° *The stomach of Archimedes.* It has been related that Archimedes worked much of his geometry from figures drawn in the ashes of the hearth and in the after-bathing oil smeared on his body. In connection with the latter, one cannot but wonder how much superb geometry may have been discovered from figures drawn on a human paunch!

77° *The death of Archimedes.* Archimedes met his end during the sack of Syracuse, and several versions of his death have been reported.

According to one account, Archimedes, unaware that Syracuse had been taken by Marcellus, was preoccupied with a diagram drawn on a sand tray when a pillaging Roman soldier entered his apartment. Seeing a shadow cast upon his diagram, Archimedes waved the intruder back and ordered him to stand clear of the figure, whereupon the incensed looter ran a spear through the old man.

Another version says that a Roman soldier entered Archimedes' study and commanded the old man to follow him to Marcellus. Archimedes, in a transport of contemplation upon a problem, declined to do so before he completed his demonstration. The enraged soldier thereupon drew his sword and ran it through the old man.

Still another version reports that a Roman soldier, running upon Archimedes, made to kill the scholar. Archimedes besought the soldier to wait a little, so that he might not leave inconclusive a problem upon which he was engaged. But the soldier, unmoved by the entreaty, instantly killed the great mathematician.

Another account relates that Archimedes was carrying some valuable mathematical instruments to Marcellus when some soldiers saw him and, thinking he carried gold in a vessel, slew the old man.

Plutarch says that nothing afflicted Marcellus so much as the death of Archimedes. The Roman general had given strict orders that no harm was to come to the great man, and one can only imagine the general's ire, and what happened to the GI who disobeyed orders.

78° *The questionable mosaic.* There is, in the Municipal Art Institute at Frankfurt am Main, a mosaic picturing a venerable scholar seated in a chair before a sand tray resting on a low table. The scholar is looking back over his shoulder at a menacing Roman soldier who, with drawn sword and a pointing arm, seems to be ordering the engaged scholar to rise and follow. There seems little doubt that this mosaic commemorates the last moments of Archimedes.

Until recently, it was believed that the mosaic had been uncovered in the floor of a room of ancient Pompeii (which was destroyed and buried in the volcanic eruption of the year 70), when that city was under excavation not many years ago. This origin of the mosaic is now believed to be fraudulent, and it is thought that the mosaic is a sixteenth-century copy of some earlier work, or perhaps is a pure falsification. Thus another pretty little story has been discredited, or at least cast into grave doubt.

79° *The tomb of Archimedes.* In his work *On the Sphere and Cylinder*, Archimedes established what are tantamount to our present-day formulas for the volume and the area of a sphere. The basic figure of the work is a sphere of radius r inscribed in a right circular cylinder of radius r and height $2r$ (see Figure 9). Archimedes showed that the volume of the sphere is exactly two thirds of the volume of the circumscribed cylinder, and the area of the sphere is exactly two thirds of the total area of the circumscribed cylinder. Archimedes was justly proud of these discoveries and expressed a wish that a figure showing a sphere with a circumscribed cylinder (like Figure 9) be engraved on his tombstone. When, with great honor and veneration, Marcellus buried the famous mathematician, he saw to it that Archimedes' request was carried out.

Many years later, in 75 B.C., when Cicero was serving as Roman quaestor in Sicily, he inquired as to the whereabouts of Archimedes' tomb. To his surprise, the Syracusans knew nothing of it and even denied that any such thing existed. With considerable effort and care

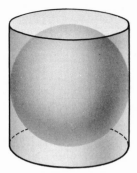

FIGURE 9

Cicero examined all the monuments, of which there were a great many, at the Achradmae gate. Finally he noticed a small column, standing out a little above overgrown briars and shrubs, with the figure of a sphere and circumscribed cylinder upon it. Thus the long-neglected and forgotten tomb of the greatest of all Syracusans was rediscovered. Cicero had men with scythes clear the brush away, and then he left orders that the surrounding grounds be restored and preserved. How long this respect was kept up we do not know; today the tomb has completely vanished.

ERATOSTHENES AND APOLLONIUS

ERATOSTHENES was a native of Cyrene on the south coast of the Mediterranean Sea and was only a few years younger than Archimedes. He spent many years of his early life in Athens and, when about forty, was invited by Ptolemy III of Egypt to come to Alexandria as tutor to his son and to serve as chief librarian at the Museum there. Most of Eratosthenes' mathematical contributions are lost, but we do know of his *sieve* for finding all the prime numbers less than a given number *n*, his mechanical "mean-finder" for duplicating the cube, and his remarkable measurement of the size of the earth. Some of Archimedes' discoveries were written up in personal letters addressed to Eratosthenes.

Apollonius, who was younger than Archimedes by some twenty-five years, was born about 262 B.C. in Perga in southern Asia Minor.

As a young man he went to Alexandria, studied under the successors of Euclid, and remained there for a long time. Later he visited Pergamum in western Asia Minor, where there was a recently founded school and library patterned after that at Alexandria. He returned to Alexandria and died there somewhere around 200 B.C. Although Apollonius was an astronomer of note and although he wrote a variety of mathematical subjects, his chief bid to fame rests on his extraordinary *Conic Sections*, a work which earned him the name, among his contemporaries, of "the Great Geometer."

80° *Eratosthenes' measurement of the earth.* Perhaps the best story that has come down to us about Eratosthenes concerns his determination of the size of the earth. Though there seems to be an element of fortuitousness in Eratosthenes' measurements, the basic idea is simple, ingenious, scientific, and appreciable by students of even the most elementary geometry or trigonometry class.

Eratosthenes learned that at noon, at the summer solstice, a vertical rod held at Syene, a city on the Nile in Egypt, casts no shadow. This fact was confirmed by noting that at that time and place the water in a deep well reflected the sun's rays directly back into the eyes of an observer looking into the well. On the other hand, at noon on the same day, a tall pillar at Alexandria was noted to cast a shadow which showed that the sun's rays there were inclined $\frac{1}{50}$ of a complete circle to the vertical. Now Eratosthenes knew that Syene lay directly south of Alexandria, at a distance of 5000 stadia. The situation we have described is pictured in Figure 10. From a simple proportion we then have

circumference of earth: $5000 = 1 : 1/50$.

It follows that

circumference of earth $= 250,000$ stadia.

There is reason to suppose that a stadium had a length of about one tenth of a mile. This leads to 25,000 miles as the approximate circumference of the earth.

It is interesting that the size of the earth was so simply and so

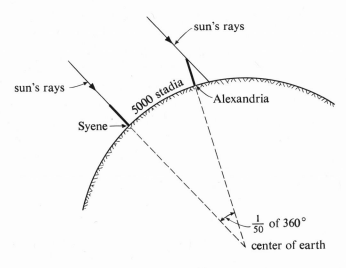

FIGURE 10

accurately determined without the use of a telescope and without traveling any great distance on land or sea.

81° *The death of Eratosthenes.* It is told that in old age Eratosthenes became either blind or almost blind from opthalmia, and, not wishing to continue life unable to read, he committed suicide by voluntary starvation.

82° *The nicknames of Eratosthenes and Apollonius.* Eratosthenes, who W. W. Rouse Ball has aptly called *the Admirable Crichton* of his age, was singularly gifted in all branches of knowledge. He was distinguished as a mathematician, an astronomer, a geographer, a historian, a philosopher, a poet, and an athlete. It is said that the students at the Museum of Alexandria used to call him *Pentathlus*, the champion in five athletic sports. He was also called *Beta*, and some speculation has been offered as to the possible origin of this nickname. Some believe it was because his broad and brilliant knowledge caused him to be looked upon as a second Plato. A less kind explanation is that, though he was gifted in many fields, he always failed to top his contemporaries in any one branch; in other words, he was always second best. Each of these explanations weakens somewhat when it is learned that a certain astronomer Apollonius, very likely Apollonius of Perga, was called *Epsilon*. Because of this, James Gow has suggested that perhaps Beta and Epsilon arose simply from the Greek numbers (2 and 5) of certain offices or lecture rooms at the Museum particularly associated with the two men. On the other hand, Ptolemy Hephaestio claimed that Apollonius was called Epsilon because he studied the moon, of which the letter ε was a symbol. Of course, the most fitting nickname for Apollonius of Perga is *the Great Geometer*, justly assigned to him by his contemporaries.

83° *The names "ellipse," "parabola," and "hyperbola."* [The following is adapted, with permission, from the article, by Howard Eves, of the same title that appeared in the Historically Speaking section of *The Mathematics Teacher*, April, 1960, pp. 280–281.]

Prior to Apollonius of Perga, the Greeks obtained the conic sections from three types of cones of revolution, according as the vertex angle of the cone was less than, equal to, or greater than a right angle. By cutting each of three such cones by planes perpendicular to a generator of the cone, an ellipse, a parabola, and a hyperbola respectively result. It follows that only one branch of a hyperbola was considered. Apollonius, on the other hand, in Book I of his great treatise *Conic Sections*, obtains all the conic sections in the now familiar way from *one* right or oblique *double* cone.

The names "ellipse," "parabola," and "hyperbola" were supplied by Apollonius, and were borrowed from the early Pythagorean terminology of application of areas. When the Pythagoreans applied a rectangle to a line segment (that is, placed the base of the rectangle along the line segment, with one end of the base coinciding with one end of the segment), they said they had a case of "ellipsis," "parabole," or "hyperbole" according as the base of the applied rectangle fell short of the line segment, exactly coincided with it, or exceeded it. Now let *AB* (see Figure 11) be the principal axis of a conic, *P* any point on the conic, and *Q* the foot of the perpendicular from *P* on *AB*. At *A*, which is a vertex of the conic, draw a perpendicular to *AB* and mark off on it a distance *AR* equal to what we now call the *latus rectum*, or *parameter p*, of the conic (that is, equal to the length of the chord

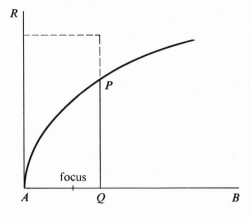

FIGURE   11

which passes through a focus of the conic and is perpendicular to the principal axis of the conic). Apply, to segment AR, a rectangle having AQ for one side and an area equal to $(PQ)^2$. According as the application falls short of, coincides with, or exceeds the segment AR, Apollonius calls the conic an *ellipse*, a *parabola*, or a *hyperbola*. In other words, if we consider the curve referred to a Cartesian coordinate system having its x and y axes along AB and AR respectively and if we designate the coordinates of P by x and y, then the curve is an ellipse if $y^2 < px$, a parabola if $y^2 = px$, and a hyperbola if $y^2 > px$. Actually, in the cases of the ellipse and hyperbola,

$$y^2 = px \mp px^2/d,$$

where d is the length of the diameter through vertex A. Apollonius derives the bulk of the geometry of the conic sections from the geometrical equivalents of these Cartesian equations.

Now an ellipse, being a closed curve lying in the finite part of the plane, has no points in common with the so-called line at infinity in the plane. The parabola, on the other hand, is tangent to the line at infinity and thus has one and only one point in common with that line, and a hyperbola intersects the line at infinity in two distinct points. Because of these relations of the three types of conics with the line at infinity, the adjectives *elliptic*, *parabolic*, and *hyperbolic* have been employed in certain parts of mathematics. Thus, in 1871, Felix Klein called the non-Euclidean geometry of Lobachevsky and Bolyai *hyperbolic geometry*, that of Riemann he called *elliptic geometry*, while the name *parabolic geometry* was reserved for Euclidean geometry. Simplifying historical origins a little, the reason for applying these three epithets to the three geometries is essentially that in the Lobachevsky–Bolyai non-Euclidean geometry there exist two distinct lines through a point P and parallel to a line l not through P, in the Riemann non-Euclidean geometry there are no lines through P parallel to l, in Euclidean geometry there is one and only one line through P parallel to l.

The three adjectives *elliptic*, *parabolic*, and *hyperbolic* are also encountered in projective geometry, and for a similar reason. In projective geometry one studies, among other things, mappings of a line upon itself defined analytically by a symmetrical equation of the form

$$Axx' + B(x + x') + C = 0.$$

Here A, B, C are real constants, and x and x' are the coordinates of corresponding points under the mapping. Such a mapping of a line upon itself is called an *involution*, and of interest in the study of an involution are those points, called *double points*, which map into themselves. To find the double points of the above involution one merely sets $x' = x$, obtaining the quadratic equation

$$Ax^2 + 2Bx + C = 0.$$

The double points of the involution are the real solutions of this quadratic equation. Since the quadratic equation has two distinct real solutions if $B^2 - AC > 0$, one and only one real solution if $B^2 - AC = 0$, and no real solutions if $B^2 - AC < 0$, the involution has come to be called *hyperbolic*, *parabolic*, and *elliptic* in the three cases respectively. Thus a hyperbolic involution has two distinct double points, a parabolic involution has one and only one double point, and an elliptic involution has no double points.

Other uses of the adjective *elliptic* in mathematics occur in the following connections: elliptic cones and cylinders, elliptic coordinates, elliptic functions, elliptic integrals, elliptic paraboloids, elliptic partial differential equations, elliptic points on a surface, and elliptic Riemann surfaces. Similarly we have hyperbolic cylinders, hyperbolic functions, hyperbolic logarithms, hyperbolic paraboloids, hyperbolic partial differential equations, hyperbolic points on a surface, hyperbolic spirals, and hyperbolic Riemann surfaces. And there are parabolic cylinders, parabolic cables, parabolic points on a surface, parabolic spirals, and parabolic Riemann surfaces. The meanings of these mathematical terms can be found, for example, in the *Mathematics Dictionary*, edited by Glenn James and R. C. James (D. Van Nostrand Co., Inc., 1959). In most cases the definitions make clear the reason for the adoption of the particular adjective employed.

DIOPHANTUS

OF tremendous importance in the history of algebra and of great influence on later European number theorists was Diophantus of Alexandria, a mathematician of uncertain date and nationality. Most historians, upon tenuous evidence, place him in the third century of our era. His most important work is his *Arithmetica*, a treatment of algebraic number theory that marks the author as a genius in this field. This work largely concerns itself with indeterminate algebraic problems where one must find only the rational solutions. Such problems have become known as *Diophantine problems*. Indeed, modern usage of the terminology generally implies the further restriction of the solution to just integers.

84° *Diophantus's personal life.*   Beyond the fact that Diophantus flourished at Alexandria, nothing certain is known about his life. There is, however, a problem in the *Greek Anthology* that purports to give us some details. The *Greek*, or *Palatine*, *Anthology* is a collection of forty-six number problems, in epigrammatic form, assembled about 500 A.D. by the grammarian Metrodorus. The problem concerning Diophantus appears as the following epitaphic summary: "Diophantus passed one sixth of his life in childhood, one twelfth in youth, and one seventh more as a bachelor. Five years after his marriage was born a son who died four years before his father, at half his father's age. [How old was Diophantus when he died?]"

If we interpret the phrase "at half his father's age" to mean "at half his father's final age," then, letting x denote Diophantus's age at death, we easily obtain the equation

$$x/6 + x/12 + x/7 + 5 + x/2 + 4 = x,$$

which gives $x = 84$. It then follows that Diophantus spent fourteen years in childhood, seven more in youth, and twelve more as a bachelor, thus marrying when he was thirty-three. Five years later, at the age of thirty-eight, he had a son who died at the age of forty-two when his father was eighty years old. If we should interpret the phrase "at half his father's age" to mean "when he was just half the age of his father," a different solution is obtained with the various episodes occurring at fractional years. Under this interpretation, Diophantus died when $65\frac{1}{3}$ years old and his son when $30\frac{2}{3}$ years old. Out of regard for Diophantus's love of integers, let us allow him and his son the longer spans of life.

85° *The syncopation of algebra.* In 1842, G. H. F. Nesselmann characterized three stages in the historical development of algebraic notation. First we have *rhetorical algebra*, in which the solution of a problem is written, without abbreviations or symbols, as a pure prose argument. Then comes *syncopated algebra*, in which stenographic abbreviations are adopted for some of the more frequently recurring quantities and operations. Finally, as the last stage, we have *symbolic algebra*, in which solutions largely appear in a mathematical shorthand made up of symbols having little apparent connection with the entities they represent. It is fairly accurate to say that algebra prior to the time of Diophantus was rhetorical. One of Diophantus's major contributions to mathematics was the syncopation of Greek algebra. Rhetorical algebra, however, persisted pretty generally in the rest of the world, with the exception of India, for many hundreds of years. Specifically, in western Europe, most algebra remained rhetorical until the fifteenth century. Symbolic algebra made its first appearance in western Europe in the sixteenth century, but did not become prevalent until the middle of the seventeenth century. It is not often realized that much of the symbolism of our elementary algebra textbooks is not more than three hundred years old.

Diophantus had abbreviations for the unknown, powers of the unknown up through the sixth, subtraction, equality, and reciprocals.

Our word "arithmetic" comes from the Greek word *arithmetike*, a compound of the words *arithmos* for "number" and *techne* for "science." It has been rather convincingly pointed out by T. L. Heath that Diophantus's symbol for the unknown was probably derived by merging the first two Greek letters, α and ρ, of the word *arithmos*. This came, in time, to look like the Greek final sigma ς. While there is doubt about this, the meaning of the notation for powers of the unknown is quite clear. Thus "unknown squared" is denoted by Δ^Υ, the first two letters of the Greek word *dunamis* ($\Delta\Upsilon$NAMIΣ) for "power." Again, "unknown cubed" is denoted by K^Υ, the first two letters of the Greek word *kubos* (KΥBOΣ) for "cube." Explanations are easily furnished for the succeeding powers of the unknown, $\Delta^\Upsilon\Delta$ (square-square), ΔK^Υ (square-cube), and $K^\Upsilon K$ (cube-cube). Diophantus's symbol for "minus" looks like an inverted V with the angle bisector drawn in. This has been explained as a compound of Λ and I, letters in the Greek word *leipis* (ΛEIΨIΣ) for "lacking." All negative terms in an expression are gathered together and preceded by the minus symbol. Addition is indicated by juxtaposition, and the coefficient of any power of the unknown is represented by the alphabetic Greek numeral following the power symbol. If there is a constant term then $\overset{\circ}{\text{M}}$, an abbreviation of the Greek word *monades* (MONAΔEΣ) for "units," is used, with the appropriate number coefficient. Thus $x^3 + 13x^2 + 5x$ and $x^3 - 5x^2 + 8x - 1$ would appear as

$$K^\Upsilon\alpha\Delta^\Upsilon\iota\gamma\varsigma\varepsilon \qquad \text{and} \qquad K^\Upsilon\alpha\varsigma\eta \wedge \Delta^\Upsilon\varepsilon\overset{\circ}{\text{M}}\alpha,$$

which can be read literally as

unknown cubed 1, unknown squared 13, unknown 5

and

(unknown cubed 1, unknown 8) minus (unknown squared 5, units 1).

It is thus that rhetorical algebra became syncopated algebra.

86° *A diophantine riddle.* The mathematician Augustus De Morgan, who lived in the nineteenth century, when asked the year of his birth, countered with: "I was x years old in the year x^2." When was he born?

87° *The Greek meaning of "arithmetic."* The ancient Greeks made a distinction between the study of the abstract relationships connecting numbers and the practical art of computing with numbers. The former was known as *arithmetic* and the latter as *logistic*. This classification persisted through the Middle Ages until about the close of the fifteenth century, when texts appeared treating both the theoretical and practical aspects of number work under the single name *arithmetic*. It is interesting that today *arithmetic* has its original significance in continental Europe, while in England and America the popular meaning of *arithmetic* is synonymous with that of ancient *logistic*, and in these two countries the descriptive term *number theory* is used to denote the abstract side of number study. In England and America, the word *logistic*, as a noun, refers to symbolic logic, and the word *logistics*, as a noun, is that branch of military art embracing the details of transporting, quartering, and supplying troops in military operations.

THE END OF THE GREEK PERIOD

The immediate successors to Euclid, Archimedes, and Apollonius prolonged the great Greek geometrical tradition for a time, but then it began steadily to languish, and new developments were limited to astronomy, trigonometry, and algebra. Then, toward the end of the third century A.D., 500 years after Apollonius, there lived the enthusiastic and competent Pappus of Alexandria, who strove to rekindle fresh interest in the subject. Although Pappus wrote a number of mathematical commentaries, his really great work is his *Mathematical Collection*, a combined commentary and guidebook of the existing geometrical works of his time, sown with numerous original propositions, improvements, extensions, and historical comments. It is a veritable mine of rich geometrical nuggets and may be called the swan song, or requiem, of Greek geometry, for after Pappus Greek mathematics ceased to be a living study and we find merely its memory perpetuated by minor writers and commentators.

88° *Some famous inequalities.* The Greeks, from early Pythagorean times on, interested themselves in three means, or averages,

called the *arithmetic*, the *geometric*, and the *subcontrary*—the last name
being later changed to *harmonic* by Archytas and Hippasus. We may
define these three means of two positive numbers a and b as

$$A = (a + b)/2, \quad G = \sqrt{ab}, \quad H = 2ab/(a + b),$$

respectively. A favorite question, often asked on a Master's oral
examination, is to show that $A \geq G \geq H$, with equality if and only if
$a = b$. A singularly neat establishment of these inequalities appears in
Book III of Pappus's *Mathematical Collection*. Take B on segment AC
(see Figure 12), and erect the perpendicular to AC at B to cut the

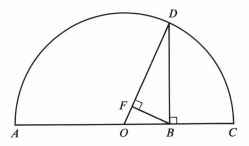

FIGURE   12

semicircle on AC in D. Then, if F is the foot of the perpendicular from
B on OD, where O is the midpoint of AC, one may easily show that OD,
BD, FD represent the arithmetic mean, the geometric mean, and the
harmonic mean of the segments AB and BC. [That OD is the arithmetic mean is obvious. That BD is the geometric mean is well known
from high school geometry. That FD is the harmonic mean follows
from the similar triangles DFB and DBO, for we have $FD/DB =
DB/OD$, whence $FD = (DB)^2/OD = 2(AB)(BC)/(AB + BC)$.] The
concerned inequalities are now geometrically evident. The Master's
candidate asked to establish these inequalities could hardly do better
than to present the Pappus argument, and he would surely make a
more impressive showing than by stumbling about with purely algebraic
procedures.

89° *Pappus's extension of the Pythagorean Theorem.* [The
following is adapted, with permission, from the article, by Howard

Eves, of the same title that appeared in the Historically Speaking section of *The Mathematics Teacher*, November, 1958, pp. 544–546.]

Every student of high school geometry sooner or later becomes familiar with the famous Pythagorean Theorem, which states that *in a right triangle the area of the square described on the hypotenuse is equal to the sum of the areas of the squares described on the two legs.* This theorem appears as Proposition 47 in Book I of Euclid's *Elements*, written about 300 B.C.

Even in Euclid's time, certain generalizations of the Pythagorean Theorem were known. For example, Proposition 31 of Book VI of the *Elements* states: *In a right triangle the area of a figure described on the hypotenuse is equal to the sum of the areas of similar figures similarly described on the two legs.* This generalization merely replaced the three squares on the three sides of the right triangle by any three similar and similarly described figures. A more worthy generalization stems from Propositions 12 and 13 of Book II. A combined and somewhat modernized statement of these two propositions is: *In a triangle, the square of the side opposite an obtuse (acute) angle is equal to the sum of the squares on the other two sides increased (decreased) by twice the product of one of these sides and the projection of the other side on it.* That is, in the notation of Figure 13, $(AB)^2 = (BC)^2 + (CA)^2 \pm 2(BC)(DC)$, the plus or minus sign being taken according as angle C of triangle ABC is obtuse or acute.

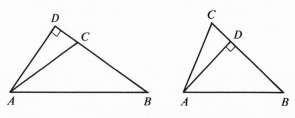

FIGURE   13

If we employ directed line segments we may combine Propositions 12 and 13 of Book II and Proposition 47 of Book I into the single statement: *If in triangle ABC, D is the foot of the altitude on side BC, then* $(AB)^2 = (BC)^2 + (CA)^2 - 2(BC)(DC)$. Since $DC = CA \cos BCA$, we recognize this last statement as essentially the so-called *law of cosines*, and the law of cosines is indeed a fine generalization of the Pythagorean Theorem.

But perhaps the most remarkable extension of the Pythagorean Theorem that dates back to the days of Greek antiquity is that given by Pappus of Alexandria at the start of Book IV of his *Mathematical Collection*. The Pappus extension of the Pythagorean Theorem is as follows (see Figure 14): *Let ABC be any triangle and CADE, CBFG any*

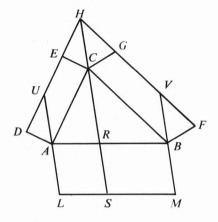

FIGURE 14

parallelograms described externally on sides CA and CB. Let DE and FG meet in H and draw AL and BM equal and parallel to HC. Then the area of parallelogram ABML is equal to the sum of the areas of parallelograms CADE and CBFG. The proof is easy, for we have $CADE = CAUH = SLAR$ and $CBFG = CBVH = SMBR$. Hence $CADE + CBFG = SLAR + SMBR = ABML$. It is to be noted that the Pythagorean Theorem has been generalized in two directions, for the right triangle in the Pythagorean Theorem has been replaced by *any* triangle, and the squares on the legs of the right triangle have been replaced by *any* parallelograms.

The student of high school geometry can hardly fail to be interested in the Pappus extension of the Pythagorean Theorem, and the proof of the extension can serve as a nice exercise for the student. Perhaps the more gifted student of geometry might like to try his hand at establishing the further extension (to three-space) of the Pappus extension: *Let ABCD* (see Figure 15) *be any tetrahedron and let ABD–EFG, BCD–HIJ, CAD–KLM be any three triangular prisms described externally on the faces ABD, BCD, CAD of ABCD. Let Q be the point of intersection of the planes*

65

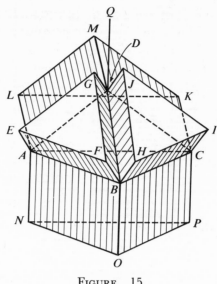

FIGURE 15

EFG, HIJ, KLM, and let ABC–NOP be the triangular prism whose edges AN, BO, CP are translates of the vector QD. Then the volume of ABC–NOP is equal to the sum of the volumes of ABD–EFG, BCD–HIJ, CAD–KLM. A proof analogous to the one given above for the Pappus extension can be supplied.

90° *The first woman mathematician.*   Among the minor writers and commentators who succeeded Pappus at the Alexandrian Museum were Theon and his daughter Hypatia. These two lived during the turbulent years of religious upheaval at the end of the fourth and the beginning of the fifth century, and they were the last scholars of mathematics at the famous institution. Theon was the author of a commentary on Ptolemy's *Almagest* and a revision of Euclid's *Elements* from which all our modern editions have derived. His daughter, Hypatia, who undoubtedly obtained an interest in mathematics from her father, is the first woman mathematician to be mentioned in the history of mathematics. She was distinguished in mathematics, medicine, and philosophy, and is reported to have written commentaries on Diophantus's *Arithmetica* and Apollonius's *Conic Sections*.

As an exponent of Alexandrian Neoplatonism, Hypatia lectured on Platonic philosophy at the Museum. Her most notable student was Synesius of Cyrene, who later became bishop of Ptolemais. His affectionate and admiring letters to Hypatia illustrate the close and fruitful contact of early *spiritual* Christianity with pagan philosophy. On the other hand, the bitter and cruel contact of early *militant* Christianity with pagan philosophy is illustrated by Hypatia's death, for in March, 415, she was seized by a mob of infuriated Christians and barbarously murdered on the steps of a pagan temple.

With the tragic passing of Hypatia, the curtain fell on the Greek contribution to mathematics; the long and glorious history of Greek mathematics essentially came to an end.

QUADRANT TWO

*From King Aśoka's columns
to a tantalizing marginal note*

HINDU MATHEMATICS

THE period starting with the fall of the Roman Empire in the middle of the fifth century and extending into the eleventh century is known as Europe's Dark Ages, for during this time civilization in western Europe reached a very low ebb. The period was marked by much physical violence and intense religious faith. Schooling became almost nonexistent and Greek learning all but disappeared. During this period, the history of mathematics, along with that of many other subjects, made a long detour through India and Arabia before it once again took up residence in western Europe.

91° *King Aśoka*. There has appeared, every now and then, a man who definitely was not a mathematician but who nevertheless played an important role in the history of mathematics. Such a man was King Aśoka, an Indian emperor from ca. 274 to ca. 232 B.C. His connection with the history of mathematics lies in the fact that some of his great stone pillars, erected in every important city of India of his day, still stand, and that some of them contain the earliest preserved specimens of our present number symbols that have come down to us.

92° *Inversion*. The Hindus were gifted arithmeticians and made significant contributions to algebra. Many of the arithmetic problems were solved by the method of *inversion*, where one works backward from a given piece of information. Consider, for example, the following problem given during the sixth century by the elder Āryabhata: "Beautiful maiden with beaming eyes, tell me, as thou understandst the right method of inversion, which is the number which multiplied by 3, then increased by $\frac{3}{4}$ of the product, then divided by 7, diminished by $\frac{1}{3}$ of the quotient, multiplied by itself, diminished by 52, by the extraction of the square root, addition of 8, and division by 10 gives the number 2?" By the method of inversion we start with the number 2 and work backward. Thus $[(2)(10) - 8]^2 + 52 = 196$, $\sqrt{196} = 14$, $(14)(\frac{3}{2})(7)(\frac{4}{7})/3 = 28$, the answer. Note that where the problem instructed us to divide by 10 we multiply by 10, where we were told to add 8 we subtract 8, where we were told to extract a square root we take the square, and so forth. It is the replacement of each operation by its inverse that accounts for the name *inversion*. It is, of course, just what we would do if we were to solve the problem by modern methods. Thus, if we let x represent the sought number, we have

$$\{\sqrt{[(\tfrac{2}{3})(\tfrac{7}{4})(3x)/7]^2 - 52} + 8\}/10 = 2.$$

To solve this we *multiply* both sides by 10, then *subtract* 8 from each side, then *square* both sides, and so forth.

93° *The rule of three.* The *rule of three*, like much else in elementary arithmetic, seems to have originated with the Hindus, and was actually called by this name by Brahmagupta (ca. 628) and Bhaskara (1114–ca. 1185). For centuries the rule was very highly regarded by merchants. It was mechanically stated without reason, and its connection with proportion was not recognized until the end of the fourteenth century. Here is how Brahmagupta stated the rule: *In the rule of three, Argument, Fruit, and Requisition are the names of the terms. The first and last terms must be similar. Requisition multiplied by Fruit, and then divided by Argument, is the Produce.* For clarification consider the following problem given by Bhaskara: If two and a half palas of saffron are purchased for three sevenths of a niska, how many palas will be purchased for nine niskas? Here $\tfrac{3}{7}$ and 9, which are of the same denomination, are the Argument and the Requisition, and $\tfrac{5}{2}$ is the Fruit. The answer, or Produce, is then given by $(9)(\tfrac{5}{2})/(\tfrac{3}{7}) = 52\tfrac{1}{2}$. Today we would regard the problem as a simple application of proportion,

$$x:9 = \tfrac{5}{2}:\tfrac{3}{7}.$$

Much space was devoted to the *rule of three* by early European writers on arithmetic, the mechanical nature of the rule being observable in the doggerel verse and schematic diagrams often used to explain it.

94° *Hindu syncopation of algebra.* The Hindus syncopated their algebra. Like Diophantus, addition was usually indicated by juxtaposition. Subtraction was indicated by placing a dot over the subtrahend, multiplication by writing *bha* (the first syllable of the word *bhavita*, "the product") after the factors, division by writing the divisor beneath the dividend, square root by writing *ka* (from the word *karana*, "irrational") before the quantity. Brahmagupta indicated the unknown by *yā* (from *yāvattāvat*, "so much as"). Known integers were prefixed by *rū* (from *rūpa*, "the absolute number"). Additional unknowns were indicated by the initial syllables of words for different colors. Thus a second unknown might be denoted by *kā* (from *kālaka*, "black"), and $8xy + \sqrt{10} - 7$ might appear as

$$yā\ kā\ 8\ bha\ ka\ 10\ rū\ \dot{7}.$$

95° *Bhaskara's daughter.* The Hindu mathematician and astronomer Bhaskara flourished around 1150. Of his works that have come down to us is an arithmetic entitled *Lilavati* ("the beautiful"), and a romantic story is told about this work. According to the tale, the stars foretold dire misfortune if Bhaskara's only daughter Lilavati should marry other than at a certain hour on a certain propitious day. On that day, as the anxious bride was watching the sinking water level of the hour cup, a pearl fell unnoticed from her headdress and, stopping the hole in the cup, arrested the outflow of water. Too late, after the unique lucky moment had passed, the accident was discovered, and the grief-stricken girl was faced with a life of spinsterhood. To console his unhappy daughter, Bhaskara gave her name to his book!

96° *Behold!* Many students of high school geometry have seen Bhaskara's dissection proof of the Pythagorean theorem, in which the square on the hypotenuse is cut up, as indicated in Figure 16, into four triangles each congruent to the given triangle plus a square with side equal to the difference of the legs of the given triangle. The pieces are easily rearranged to give the sum of the squares on the two legs. Bhaskara drew the figure and offered no further explanation than the

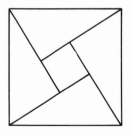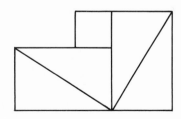

FIGURE   16

word "Behold!" Of course, a little algebra supplies a proof. For, if c is the hypotenuse and a and b are the legs of the triangle,

$$c^2 = 4(\tfrac{1}{2}ab) + (b - a)^2 = a^2 + b^2.$$

Perhaps a better "behold" proof of the Pythagorean theorem would be a dynamical one on movie film wherein the square on the hypotenuse is continuously transformed into the sum of the squares on the legs by passing through the stages indicated in Figure 17.

97° *Hindu embroidery.* The Hindus often clothed their arithmetic problems in poetic garb. This was partly because school texts were, for purposes of memorization, written in verse, but particularly because the problems were so frequently propounded as puzzles for sheer social amusement. As a couple of examples, consider the following; the first is adapted from Bhaskara (ca. 1150) and the second from Mahavira(ca. 850).

> The square root of half the number of bees in a swarm has flown out upon a jessamine bush, $\tfrac{8}{9}$ of the swarm has remained behind; one female bee flies about a male that is buzzing within a lotus flower into which he was allured in the night by its sweet odor, but is now imprisoned in it. Tell me, most enchanting lady, the number of bees.

> Into the bright and refreshing outskirts of a forest, which were full of numerous trees with their branches bent down with the weight of flowers and fruits, trees such as jambu trees, lime trees, plantains, areca palms, jack trees, date palms, hintala trees, palmyras, punnago trees, and mango trees—outskirts, the various quarters whereof were filled with many sounds of crowds of parrots and cuckoos found near springs containing lotuses with bees roaming about them—into such forest outskirts a number of weary travelers entered with joy. There were 63 numerically equal heaps of plantain fruits put together and combined with 7 more of those same fruits, and these were equally distributed among 23 travelers so as to have no remainder. You tell me now the numerical measure of a heap of plantains.

Brahmagupta, in connection with his problem offerings, says: "These problems are proposed simply for pleasure; the wise man can invent a thousand others, or he can solve the problems of others by the rules given here. As the sun eclipses the stars by his brilliancy, so the man of knowledge will eclipse the fame of others in assemblies of

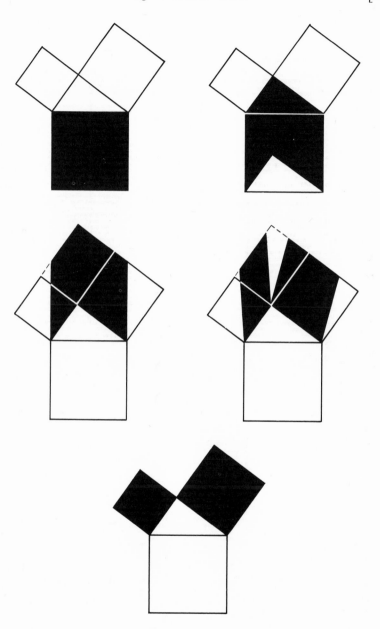

FIGURE 17

the people if he proposes algebraic problems, and still more if he solves them."

Of interest is an early-used *symbolical system of position*, in which numbers were often expressed by suggestive objects. Thus, for 1 might appear the word *moon*, or *Brahma*, or *Creator*, or *form*; for 4, the word *Veda* (because this book was divided into four parts), or *ocean*. As an example, consider the following found in the *Surya Siddhanta*, an anonymous work on astronomy that dates from perhaps the beginning of the fifth century. The number 1,577,917,828 is expressed, from right to left, as: Vasu (a class of eight gods) + two + eight + mountains (the seven mountain ranges) + form + digits (the nine digits) + seven + mountains + lunar days (half of which equals fifteen). Such practice made it possible to represent a number in many different ways, thus greatly facilitating the framing of verses containing arithmetical rules or scientific constants, and making such rules or constants more easy to remember.

98° *Buddha's examination.*   Even the very early Hindus exhibited great skill in calculating with large numbers. Thus we are told of an examination to which Buddha, the great religious teacher of about the sixth century B.C., had to submit, in his youth, in order to win the hand of the maiden he loved. He was asked to determine the number of primary atoms which, when placed side by side, would form a line one "mile" long. Buddha found the required number as follows: seven primary atoms make a very minute grain of dust, seven of these make a minute grain of dust, seven of these a grain of dust whirled up by the wind, and so on. He proceeded thus, step by step, until he finally reached the length of one "mile." The product of the factors gave a number of fifteen digits.

99° *False position in the Bakshali manuscript.*   An anonymous arithmetic, known as the *Bakshali manuscript*, was unearthed in 1881 at Bakshali, in northwest India. It consists of seventy pages of birch bast. Its origin and date have been the subject of much conjecture, estimates of the date ranging from the third to the twelfth century A.D. Some of the problems of the Bakshali manuscript are solved by a reduction to unity, or a sort of *rule of false position*. As an example we find: *B* gives twice as much as *A*, *C* three times as much as *B*, *D* four times as much as *C*; together they give 132; how much did *A* give? Take 1 for the unknown. Then the amount given by *A* is 1, that given by *B* is 2, that by *C* is 6, that by *D* is 24, and the sum of these is 33. Divide 132 by 33; the quotient 4 is what *A* gave.

100° *Contrast between Greek and Hindu mathematics.*   There are many differences between Greek and Hindu mathematics. In the first place, the Hindus who worked in mathematics regarded themselves primarily as astronomers, and thus Hindu mathematics remained largely a handmaiden to astronomy; with the Greeks, mathematics attained an independent existence and was studied for its own sake. Also, due to the caste system, mathematics in India was cultivated almost entirely by the priests; in Greece, mathematics was open to any who cared to study the subject. Again, the Hindus were accomplished computers but mediocre geometers; the Greeks excelled in geometry but, in general, cared little for computational work. Even Hindu trigonometry, which was meritorious, was arithmetical in nature; Greek trigonometry was geometrical in character. The Hindus wrote in verse and often clothed their works in obscure and mystic language; the Greeks strove for clarity and logicality in presentation. Hindu mathematics is largely empirical with proofs or derivations seldom offered; an outstanding characteristic of Greek mathematics is its insistence on rigorous demonstration. Hindu mathematics is of very uneven quality, good and poor mathematics often appearing side by side; the Greeks seemed to have an instinct that led them to distinguish good from poor quality and to preserve the former while abandoning the latter.

A good deal of the contrast between Greek and Hindu mathematics is perpetuated today in the differences between many of our elementary geometry and algebra textbooks. We owe our geometry to the Greeks, our algebra to the Hindus. Only recently, with the emphasis on the "new mathematics," have our algebra textbooks begun to attain a rigor, a logicality, and a qualitative selectiveness of material comparable to that found in the elementary geometry texts.

101° *Srinivasa Ramanujan.* Perhaps the most spectacular Indian mathematician of modern times has been the impoverished clerk and untrained genius Srinivasa Ramanujan (1887–1920), who possessed amazing ability to see quickly and deeply into intricate number relations. He was "discovered" in 1913 by the eminent British number theorist G. H. Hardy (1877–1947), whose efforts brought Ramanujan in the following year to England to study at Cambridge University. There resulted a most remarkable mathematical association between the two men.

The most frequently told story illustrating Ramanujan's uncanny abilities is about a visit once made by Hardy when Ramanujan was ill in a hospital at Putney. Hardy arrived at the hospital in a taxi bearing the seemingly dull number 1729. Hardy took down the number and, in curiosity, asked Ramanujan if there is anything interesting about it. Without hesitation Ramanujan said there certainly is, inasmuch as it is the smallest positive integer that can be represented in two different ways as a sum of two cubes—$1729 = 1^3 + 12^3 = 9^3 + 10^3$.

Ramanujan had the same preternatural ability with numbers that was possessed by his early predecessors, and his work exhibited the same disorganized character, strong intuition, and slighting of deductive processes also found in the earlier men's work. Ramanujan might almost be called a twentieth-century Bhaskara. We see in Ramanujan's work many of the differences between early Hindu and Greek mathematics. Of course, much of this may be traced to the fact that Ramanujan was largely unsystematically self-taught.

ARABIAN MATHEMATICS

OF considerable importance for the preservation of much of world culture was the manner in which the Arabs seized upon Greek and Hindu erudition. The Baghdad caliphs not only governed well, but many became patrons of learning and invited distinguished scholars to their courts. Numerous Hindu and Greek works in astronomy, medicine, and mathematics were industriously translated into the Arabic tongue and thus were saved until later European scholars were able to retranslate them into Latin and other languages. But for the work of the Arabian scholars much of Greek and Hindu science would have been irretrievably lost over the long period of the Dark Ages.

102° *Arabian names in astronomy.* Many names and words used today may be traced back to the Arabian period. Thus anyone interested in observational astronomy probably is aware that a large number of star names, particularly those of the fainter stars, are Arabic. As well-known examples we have Aldebaran, Vega, and Rigel among the brighter stars, and Algol, Alcor, and Mizar among the fainter ones. Many of the star names were originally expressions locating the stars in the constellations. These descriptive expressions, when translated from Ptolemy's catalogue into the Arabic, later degenerated into single words. Thus we have Betelgeuse (armpit of the Central One), Fomalhaut (mouth of the Fish), Deneb (tail of the Bird), Rigel (leg of the Giant), and so forth.

The definitive Greek work on astronomy was written by Claudius Ptolemy of Alexandria about 150 A.D. This very influential treatise, called the *Syntaxis mathematica*, or "Mathematical Collection," was based on the writings of Hipparchus and is noted for its remarkable compactness and elegance. To distinguish it from lesser works on astronomy, later commentators assigned to it the superlative *magiste*, or "greatest." Still later, the Arabian translators prefixed the Arabian article *al*, and the work has ever since been known as the *Almagest*.

103° *The origin of our word "algebra."* Very interesting is the origin of our word *algebra* from the title, *Hisâb al-jabr w'al-muqâbalah*, of al-Khowârizmî's treatise (ca. 825) on the subject. This title has been literally translated as "science of the reunion and the opposition," or more freely as "science of reduction and cancellation." The text, which is extant, became known in Europe through Latin translations, and made the word *al-jabr*, or *algebra*, synonymous with the science of equations. Since the middle of the nineteenth century, *algebra* has come, of course, to mean a great deal more.

The Arabic word *al-jabr*, used in a nonmathematical sense, found its way into Europe through the Moors of Spain. There an *algebrista* was a bonesetter (reuniter of broken bones), and it was usual for a barber of the times to call himself an *algebrista,* for bonesetting and bloodletting were sidelines of the medieval barber.

104° *The origin of our word "algorithm."* In addition to a treatise on algebra, al-Khowârizmî wrote a book on the use of the Hindu numerals, and this second work has also introduced a word into the vocabulary of mathematics. The book is not extant in the original, but in 1857 a Latin translation was found that begins, "Spoken has Algoritmi, ..." Here the name *al-Khowârizmî* has become *Algoritmi,* from which, in turn, was derived our present word "algorism," or "algorithm," meaning the art of calculating in any particular way.

105° *The origin of our word "zero."* Our word *zero* probably comes from the Latinized form *zephirum* of the Arabic *sifr,* which in turn is a translation of the Hindu *sunya,* meaning "void" or "empty." The Arabic *sifr* was introduced into Germany in the thirteenth century by Nemorarius, as *cifra,* from which we have obtained our present word *cipher.*

106° *The origin of our word "sine."* The meanings of the present names of the trigonometric functions, with the exception of *sine,* are clear from their geometrical interpretations when the angle is placed at the center of a circle of unit radius. Thus, in Figure 18, if the radius of the circle is one unit, the measures of tan θ and sec θ are given by the lengths of the *tangent* segment *CD* and the *secant* segment *OD.* And, of course, *cotangent* merely means *c*omplement's tangent, and so on. The functions tangent, cotangent, secant, and cosecant have been known by various other names, these present ones appearing as late as the end of the sixteenth century.

The origin of the word *sine* is curious. Āryabhata called it *ardhā-jyā* ("half chord") and also *jyā-ardhā* ("chord half"), and then abbreviated the term by simply using *jyā* ("chord"). From *jyā* the Arabs phonetically derived *jîba,* which, following the Arabian practice of omitting vowel symbols, was written as *jb.* Now *jîba,* aside from its technical significance, is a meaningless word in Arabic. Later writers, coming across *jb* as an abbreviation for the meaningless *jîba* decided to sub-

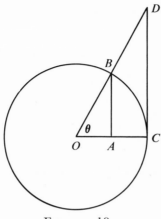

FIGURE   18

stitute *jaib* instead, which contains the same letters and is a good Arabian word meaning "cove" or "bay." Still later, Gherardo of Cremona (ca. 1150), when he made his translations from the Arabic, replaced the Arabic *jaib* by its Latin equivalent, *sinus*, whence came our present word *sine*.

107° *Alhazen's madness.* The name al-Haytham or, more popularly today, Alhazen (ca. 965–1039) has been preserved in mathematics in connection with the so-called *problem of Alhazen*: to draw from two given points in the plane of a given circle lines that intersect on the circle and make equal angles with the circle at that point. The problem leads to a quartic equation that was solved in Greek fashion by an intersecting hyperbola and circle; the problem, like the trisection of a general angle, is beyond the Euclidean tools. Alhazen was born at Basra in South Iraq and was perhaps the greatest of the Moslem physicists. The above problem arose in connection with his *Optics*, a treatise that later had great influence in Europe.

Alhazen unfortunately once boasted that he could construct a machine that would control and regulate the annual inundation of the Nile River. He was accordingly summoned to Egypt by Caliph Hakim to explain and perhaps demonstrate his idea. Aware of the utter impracticality of his scheme, and fearing the anger of the Caliph,

Alhazen feigned madness, for the insane were specially protected in those times. With great care, Alhazen had to keep up the hoax until Hakim's death in 1021.

108° *The three students.* Perhaps the deepest and most original contribution to Arabian algebra was the geometrical solution of cubic equations by Omar Khayyam (ca. 1044–ca. 1123), a native of Khorasan, and known to the Western world through Edward Fitzgerald as the author of the exquisite *Rubaiyat*. Khayyam is also noted for his work on the calendar reform and for a critical treatment of Euclid's *Elements* in which he appears as a forerunner of Saccheri's ideas that finally led to the creation of the first non-Euclidean geometry.

A thought-provoking story has come down to us about Omar Khayyam and two of his schoolmates. In their youth, Nizam ul Mulk, Hasan Ben Sabbah, and Omar Khayyam studied together as pupils of one of the greatest wise men of Khorasan, the Imam Mowaffak of Naishapur. The three youths, all very capable scholars, became close friends. Since it was the belief that a pupil of the Imam stood great chance of attaining fortune, Hasan one day proposed to his friends that the three of them take a vow to the effect that to whomever of them fortune should fall, he would share it equally with the others and reserve no pre-eminence for himself. As the years went by, Nizam proved to be the fortunate one, for he became Vizier to the Sultan Alp Arslan. In time his school friends sought him out and claimed a share of his good fortune according to the school-day vow.

Hasan demanded a governmental post, which was granted by the Sultan at the Vizier's request. But, being selfish and ungrateful, he endeavored to supplant his friend Nizam and was finally disgraced and banished. Omar desired neither title nor office, but simply begged to be permitted to live in the shadow of the Vizier's fortune, where he might promulgate science and mathematics and pray for his friend's long life and prosperity. Impressed by his former schoolmate's modesty and sincerity, the Vizier granted Omar a yearly pension.

After many misadventures and wandering, Hasan became the head of a party of fanatics who, in 1090, seized the castle of Alamut in the mountainous area south of the Caspian Sea. Using the castle as a fortress and center for raids upon passing caravans, Hasan and his band spread terror through the Mohammedan world. Hasan became known as "the old man of the mountain," and it is thought that our present word "assassin" derives either from the leader's name *Hasan* or from the *hashish* opiate with which the band maddened themselves for their murderous assaults. Among the countless victims of the assassins was the old school friend, Nizam ul Mulk.

In contrast to Hasan's turbulent and destructive life, Omar's was tranquil and constructive. He lived peacefully and contributed noteworthily to both the literary and the scientific culture of his age.

So, of the three students, one turned out to be a fine administrator and benefactor, one a miserable renegade and murderer, and one a devoted scholar and creator. Somehow the world at large seems reflected here. If only we could make the odds in favor of the good better than two to one!

109° *Omar's roses.*   Omar Khayyam died in Naishapur about 1123. A pupil of his, one Khwajah Nizami of Samarcand, has related that he used to converse with his teacher Omar in a garden, and that Omar once said that his tomb would be located in a spot where the north wind would scatter rose petals over it. Some years later, after the death of his teacher, the former pupil chanced to visit Naishapur and he searched out the master's grave. It was just outside a garden. Boughs of fruit trees hanging over the garden wall had dropped so many blossoms on the grave that the tombstone was completely hidden.

When Edward Fitzgerald, the sympathetic Irish translator who made Omar Khayyam so famous in modern times, passed away in 1883, he was buried in a little English churchyard at Boulge, Suffolk. In 1884, William Simpson, a traveling artist of the *Illustrated London News*, visited Naishapur and found the not-quite-neglected tomb of Omar. Along the edge of the platform in front of the tomb he found some rose-trees and he plucked from these a few of the hips still hanging on the bushes. These seeds, when they arrived in England, were handed over to Mr. Baker of the Kew Botanical Gardens, who planted them and successfully grew some rose-trees from them. On October 7, 1893, one of these rose-trees was transplanted to Fitzgerald's graveside.

Look to the blowing Rose about us—"Lo,
Laughing," she says, "into the world I blow,
   At once the silken tassel of my Purse
Tear, and its Treasure on the Garden throw."

THE RETURN OF MATHEMATICS TO WESTERN EUROPE

TOWARD the end of the tenth century, Greek classics in science and mathematics began to filter into western Europe. There followed a period of transmission during which the ancient learning preserved by Moslem culture was passed on to the western Europeans. This took place through Latin translations made by Christian scholars traveling to Moslem centers of learning, through the relations between the Norman kingdom of Sicily and the east, and through western European commercial relations with the Levant and the Arabic world.

110° *Gerbert, Pope Sylvester II.* The period starting with the fall of the Roman Empire in the middle of the fifth century and extending into the eleventh century is known as Europe's Dark Ages, for during this period civilization in western Europe reached a very low ebb. Schooling became almost nonexistent, Greek learning all but disappeared, and many of the arts and crafts bequeathed by the ancient world were forgotten. Only the monks of the Christian monasteries, and a few cultured laymen, preserved a slender thread of Greek and Latin learning. The period was marked by much physical violence and intense religious faith. The old order gave way and society became feudal and ecclesiastical.

The Romans had never taken to abstract mathematics, but contented themselves with merely practical aspects of the subject associated with commerce and civil engineering. With the fall of the Roman Empire and the subsequent closing down of much of East–West trade and the abandonment of state engineering projects, even these interests waned, and it is no exaggeration to say that very little in mathematics, beyond the development of the Christian calendar, was accomplished in the West during the whole of the half millennium covered by the Dark Ages.

Of the persons charitably credited with playing a role in the history of mathematics during the Dark Ages, perhaps the greatest was the famous French scholar and churchman Gerbert, who became Pope Sylvester II.

Gerbert was born about 950 in Auvergne, France, and early showed unusual abilities. He was one of the first Christians to study in the Moslem schools of Spain and there is evidence that he may have brought back the Hindu-Arabic numerals, without the zero, to Christian Europe. He possessed great manual talent, and constructed abaci, terrestrial and celestial globes, a clock, and perhaps an organ. Such accomplishments corroborated the suspicions of some of his contemporaries that he had traded his soul to the devil, and fables began to cluster about his name similar to those that later gathered around Faust. There is a story of a speaking statue that foretold Gerbert would die at Jerusalem—a prophecy that was fulfilled (somewhat as in the case of Henry IV of England) by his dying in the Jerusalem church of Rome. In spite of the legends, he steadily rose in the Church and was finally elevated to the papacy in 999. As he successfully steered the Church through the ominous year 1000, he became the first of a long line of so-called magician popes. He died in 1003.

111° *The century of translators.* The loss of Toledo by the Moors to the Christians in 1085 was followed by an influx of Christian scholars to that city to acquire Moslem learning. Other Moorish centers in Spain were infiltrated and the twelfth century became, in the history of mathematics, a century of translators. One of the earliest Christian scholars to engage in this pursuit was the English monk Adelard of Bath (ca. 1120), who studied in Spain and traveled extensively through Greece, Syria, and Egypt. Adelard is credited with Latin translations of Euclid's *Elements* and of al-Khowârizmî's astronomical tables. There are thrilling allusions to the physical risks run by Adelard in his acquisition of Arabic learning; to obtain the jealously guarded knowledge, he disguised himself as a Mohammedan student. Another early translator was the Italian, Plato of Tivoli (ca. 1120), who translated the astronomy of al-Battânî, the *Spherics* of Theodosius, and various other works. The most industrious translator of the period was Gherardo of Cremona (1114–1187), who translated into Latin over ninety Arabian works, among which were Ptolemy's *Almagest*, Euclid's *Elements*, and al-Khowârizmî's algebra. We have already, in Item 106°, mentioned the part played by Gherardo of Cremona in the development of our word *sine*. Other noted translators of the twelfth century were John of Seville and Robert of Chester.

112° *The Norman kingdom of Sicily.* The location and political history of Sicily made that island a natural meeting ground of East and West. Sicily started as a Greek colony, became part of the Roman Empire, linked itself with Constantinople after the fall of Rome, was held by the Arabs for about fifty years in the ninth century, was recaptured by the Greeks, and was then taken over by the Normans. During the Norman regime the Greek, Arabian, and Latin tongues were used side by side, and diplomats frequently traveled to Constantinople and Baghdad. Many Greek and Arabian manuscripts in science and mathematics were obtained and translated into Latin. This work was greatly encouraged by the two rulers and patrons of science, Frederick II (1194–1250) and his son Manfred (ca. 1231–1266).

113° *The Italian commercial centers.* Among the first cities to establish mercantile relations with the Arabic world were the Italian commercial centers of Genoa, Pisa, Venice, Milan, and Florence. Italian merchants came in contact with much of Eastern civilization, picking up useful arithmetical and algebraical information. These merchants played an important part in the dissemination of the Hindu-Arabic numeral system.

114° *From rabbits to sunflowers.* At the threshold of the thirteenth century appeared Leonardo Fibonacci ("Leonardo, son of Bonaccio"), perhaps the most talented mathematician of the Middle Ages. Also known as Leonardo of Pisa (or Leonardo Pisano), Fibonacci was born in the commercial center of Pisa, where his father was connected with the mercantile business. Many of the large Italian businesses in those days maintained warehouses in various parts of the Mediterranean world. It was in this way, when his father was serving as a customs manager, that young Leonardo was brought up in Bougie on the north coast of Africa. The father's occupation early roused in the boy an interest in arithmetic, and subsequent extended trips to Egypt, Sicily, Greece, and Syria brought him in contact with Eastern and Arabic mathematical practices. Thoroughly convinced of the practical superiority of the Hindu-Arabic methods of calculation Fibonacci, in 1202, shortly after his return home, published his famous work called the *Liber abaci*.

The *Liber abaci* is known to us through a second edition that appeared in 1228. The work is devoted to arithmetic and elementary algebra and, though essentially an independent investigation, shows the influence of al-Khowârizmî and Abû Kâmil. The book profusely illustrates and strongly advocates the Hindu-Arabic notation and did much to aid the introduction of these numerals into Europe.

The *Liber abaci* contains a large collection of problems that served later authors as a storehouse for centuries. We have already, in Item 13°, mentioned one interesting problem from the collection, which apparently evolved from a much older problem in the Rhind papyrus. But perhaps the most fruitful problem in the work is the following: "How many pairs of rabbits can be produced from a single pair in a year if every month each pair begets a new pair which from the second month on becomes productive?" Without much effort, the reader can show that this problem leads to the following interesting sequence (wherein the terms are the number of pairs of rabbits present in successive months),

$$1, 1, 2, 3, 5, \ldots, x, y, x + y, \ldots.$$

This sequence, in which the first two terms are 1's and then each succeeding term is the sum of the two immediately preceding ones, has become known as the *Fibonacci sequence* and it has appeared in an astonishing number of unexpected places. It has applications to dissection puzzles, art, and phyllotaxis, and it appears surprisingly in various parts of mathematics.

Consider, for example, the seed head of a sunflower. The seeds are found in small diamond-shaped pockets bounded by spiral curves radiating from the center of the head to the outside edge, as illustrated in Figure 19. Now the curious thing is this, if one should count the number of clockwise spirals and then the number of counterclockwise spirals, these two numbers will be found to be successive terms in the

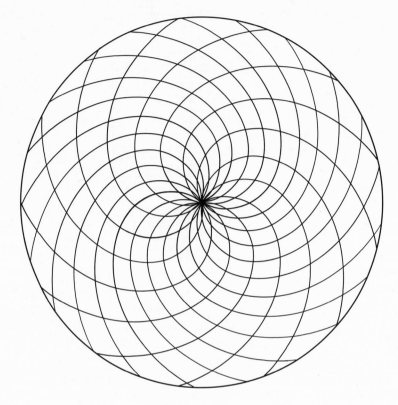

FIGURE   19

Fibonacci sequence. Indeed, this is true of the seed head of any composite flower (for instance a daisy, or an aster); it is more easily tested
on a sunflower because these flowers have such large seeds and seed
heads. Incidentally, as a further curiosity, the above-mentioned spirals
are logarithmic spirals.

Next consider the leaves (or buds, or branches) growing out of the
side of a stalk of a plant. If we fix our attention on some leaf near the
bottom of the stalk and then count the number of leaves up the stalk
until we come to one that is directly over the original leaf, this number
is generally a term of the Fibonacci sequence. Also, as we work up the
stalk and count the number of times we revolve about the stalk before
we come to a leaf directly over the original one, this number is generally

the preceding alternate term of the sequence. Similar arrangements occur in a wide variety of plant forms, such as in the leaves of a head of lettuce, in the layers of an onion, and in the conical spirals of a pine cone.

If we form the sequence of ratios of successive terms of the Fibonacci sequence, we obtain

$$\frac{1}{1}, \frac{1}{2}, \frac{2}{3}, \frac{3}{5}, \frac{5}{8}, \frac{8}{13}, \cdots$$

It can be shown mathematically that this sequence of ratios approaches the number

$$r = (\sqrt{5} - 1)/2$$

as a limit. This is the famous so-called *golden ratio* that interested the Greeks of a couple of thousand years ago. The Greeks said that a line segment AC is divided into the golden ratio by the point B if $AB/BC = BC/AC$. In this case it can be shown that each of the ratios AB/BC and BC/AC is equal to r. It seems that nature strives to approximate the golden ratio r.

Psychological tests have shown that to most people the rectangle that appears most pleasing to the eye is the one whose ratio of width to length is the golden ratio r. This rectangle, which may be called the *golden rectangle*, is fundamental in an art technique known as "dynamic symmetry," which has been intensively studied by Jay Hambidge and others. The golden ratio and the golden rectangle have been observed in Greek architecture and Greek pottery, and have been applied to sculpture, painting, architectural design, furniture design, and type display. A number of artists, such as the well known American painter George Bellows, have extensively used the principles of dynamic symmetry in their work.

The Fibonacci sequence finds many unexpected uses in various parts of mathematical study. For instance, there is a computational process, called the *Euclidean algorithm*, for finding the greatest common divisor of two given positive integers. The process requires a number of successive divisions. This number of divisions is relatively small when compared with the magnitudes of the two given positive integers. It is natural to wonder if it is possible to establish a priori a limit for the number of divisions. The answer is given by the following neat theorem due to Gabriel Lamé (1795–1870): *The number of divisions required to find the greatest common divisor of two positive integers is never greater than five times the number of digits in the smaller number.* Now the proof of this theorem utilizes, of all things, some properties of the Fibonacci sequence!

The literature on the Fibonacci sequence and its many properties is incredibly large and continues to grow. The interesting relations seem, like the geometry of the triangle, to be inexhaustible. In fact, in 1963, a group of Fibonacci-sequence enthusiasts, headed by Dr. Verner Hoggatt, Jr., founded the Fibonacci Association and began publication of a journal, *The Fibonacci Quarterly*, devoted principally to research on the Fibonacci sequence. In its first three years of existence, this journal published close to 1000 pages of research in this particular field. In 1968, three extra issues of the journal appeared in a desperate effort to catch up somewhat on the large manuscript backlog.

115° *A mathematical tournament.* Fibonacci's mathematical talents came to the attention of the patron of learning, Emperor Frederick II of the Norman kingdom of Sicily, with the result that Fibonacci was invited to court to partake in a mathematical tournament. Three problems were set by John of Palermo, a member of the emperor's retinue. Fibonacci solved all three problems, a performance that evoked considerable admiration.

The first problem was to find a rational number x such that $x^2 + 5$ and $x^2 - 5$ shall each be squares of rational numbers. Fibonacci gave the answer $x = \frac{41}{12}$, which is correct, since $\left(\frac{41}{12}\right)^2 + 5 = \left(\frac{49}{12}\right)^2$ and $\left(\frac{41}{12}\right)^2 - 5 = \left(\frac{31}{12}\right)^2$.

The second problem was to find a solution to the cubic equation

$$x^3 + 2x^2 + 10x = 20.$$

Fibonacci attempted a proof that no root of the equation can be expressed by means of irrationalities of the form $\sqrt{(a + \sqrt{b})}$, or, in other words, that no root can be constructed with straightedge and compasses. He then obtained an approximate answer, which, expressed in decimal notation, is

1.3688081075,

and is correct to nine places. There has been expression of wonder as to how Fibonacci found this answer.

The third problem, which is the easiest of the three, was as follows: "Three men possess a pile of money, their shares being $\frac{1}{2}$, $\frac{1}{3}$, $\frac{1}{6}$. Each man takes some money from the pile until nothing is left. The first man then returns $\frac{1}{2}$ of what he took, the second $\frac{1}{3}$, and the third $\frac{1}{6}$. When the total so returned is divided equally among the men it is found that each then possesses what he is entitled to. How much money was in the original pile, and how much did each man take from the pile?" Here is essentially Fibonacci's solution to the problem. Let s denote the original sum and $3x$ the total sum returned. Before each man received a third of the sum returned, the three men possessed $s/2 - x$, $s/3 - x$, $s/6 - x$. Since these are the sums they possessed after putting back $\frac{1}{2}$, $\frac{1}{3}$, $\frac{1}{6}$ of what they had first taken, the amounts first taken were $2(s/2 - x)$, $\frac{3}{2}(s/3 - x)$, $\frac{6}{5}(s/6 - x)$, and these amounts added together equal s. Therefore $7s = 47x$, and the problem is indeterminate. Fibonacci took $s = 47$ and $x = 7$. Then the sums taken by the men from the original pile are 33, 13, 1.

116° *The blockhead.* Fibonacci sometimes signed his work with *Leonardo Bigollo.* Now *bigollo* has more than one meaning; it means both "traveler" and "blockhead." In signing his work as he did, Fibonacci may have meant that he was a great traveler, for so he was. But a story has circulated that he took pleasure in using this signature because many of his contemporaries considered him a blockhead (for his interest in the new numbers), and it pleased him to show these critics what a blockhead could accomplish.

117° *Finger numbers.* In addition to spoken numbers, *finger numbers* were at one time widely used. Indeed, the expression of numbers by various positions of the fingers and hands probably predates the use of either number symbols or number names. Thus the early written symbols for one, two, three, and four were invariably the suitable number of vertical or horizontal strokes, representing the corresponding number of raised or extended fingers, and the word *digit* (that is, *finger*) for the numbers one through nine can be traced to the same source.

In time finger numbers were extended to include the largest

numbers occurring in commercial transactions, and by the Middle Ages they had become international. In the ultimate development in Europe, the numbers 1, 2, ... , 9 and 10, 20, ... , 90, were represented on the left hand, and the numbers 100, 200, ... , 900 and 1000, 2000, ... , 9000 on the right hand. In this way, any number up to 10,000 was representable by the use of the two hands. Pictures of the finger numbers were given in later arithmetic books. For example, using the left hand, one was represented by partially folding down the little finger, two by partially folding down the little and ring fingers, three by partially folding down the little, ring, and middle fingers, four by folding down the middle and ring fingers, five by folding down the middle finger, six by folding down the ring finger, seven by completely folding down the little finger, eight by completely folding down the little and ring fingers, and nine by completely folding down the little, ring, and middle fingers.

With the above information, the reader can now explain the ninth-century riddle that is sometimes attributed to Alcuin (ca. 775): I saw a man holding eight in his hand, and from the eight he took seven, and six remained. He can also explain the following, found in Juvenal's tenth satire: "Happy is he indeed who has postponed the hour of his death so long and finally numbers his years upon his right hand."

Finger numbers had the advantage of transcending language differences, but, like the vocal numbers, they lacked permanence and were not suitable for performing extended calculations. Nevertheless, there did develop finger processes for certain simple computations. One of these processes, by giving the product of two numbers each between 5 and 10, served to reduce the memory work connected with the multiplication tables. For example, to multiply 7 by 9, raise $7 - 5 = 2$ fingers on one hand and $9 - 5 = 4$ fingers on the other hand. Now add the raised fingers, $2 + 4 = 6$, for the tens digit of the product, and multiply the closed fingers, $3 \times 1 = 3$, for the units digit of the product, giving the result 63. This process is still used by some European peasants, and the reader is invited to prove that the method gives correct results.

118° *The eulogist of mathematics.* Roger Bacon (ca. 1214–ca. 1294), original genius that he was, had little ability in mathematics but was acquainted with many of the Greek works in geometry and astronomy, and, as his eulogies attest, fully appreciated the value of the subject. It was in his *Opus Majus* that he made what has become his best known panegyric on mathematics: "Mathematics is the gate and key of the sciences.... Neglect of mathematics works injury to all knowledge, since he who is ignorant of it cannot know the other sciences or the things of this world. And what is worse, men who are thus ignorant are unable to perceive their own ignorance and so do not seek a remedy."

119° *Submathematical analysis.* Although European mathematics during the Middle Ages was essentially practical, speculative mathematics did not entirely die out. The meditations of scholastic philosophers led to subtle theorizing on motion, the infinitely large and the infinitely small, the continuous and the discrete, all of which are fundamental concepts in modern mathematics. The centuries of scholastic disputes and quibblings may, to some extent, account for the remarkable transformation from ancient to modern mathematical thinking, and might, as suggested by E. T. Bell, constitute a *submathematical analysis.* From this point of view, Thomas Aquinas (1226–1274), perhaps possessing the most acute mind of the thirteenth century, can well be considered as having played a part in the development of mathematics.

THE FOURTEENTH, FIFTEENTH, AND SIXTEENTH CENTURIES

THE fourteenth century was a mathematically barren one. It was the century of the Black Death, which swept away more than a third of the population of Europe, and in this century the Hundred Years' War, with its political and economical upheavals in northern Europe, got well under way.

The fifteenth century witnessed the start of the European Renaissance in art and learning. With the collapse of the Byzantine Empire, culminating in the fall of Constantinople to the Turks in 1453, refugees flowed into Italy bringing with them treasures of Greek civilization. Many Greek classics, hitherto known only through the often inadequate

Arabic translations, could now be studied from original sources. Also, about the middle of the century, printing was invented and revolutionized the book trade, enabling knowledge to be disseminated at an unprecedented rate. Toward the end of the century, America was discovered and soon the earth was circumnavigated. Mathematical activity was largely centered in the Italian cities and in the central European cities of Nuremberg, Vienna, and Prague, under the influence of trade, navigation, astronomy, and surveying.

In the sixteenth century the development of arithmetic and algebra continued, the most spectacular mathematical achievement of the century being the discovery, by Italian mathematicians, of the algebraic solution of cubic and quartic equations. Algebra began to pass from the syncopated stage into the symbolic stage.

120° *The mechanical eagle.* Some men eminent in the history of mathematics achieved additional fame as inventors or constructors of various mechanical devices. One recalls Archimedes (ca. 287–212 B.C.) and his screw pump and devices to defend Syracuse against the Romans. And there was Heron of Alexandria (75?), that encyclopedic writer on mathematical and physical subjects, who designed some hundred machines and toys, such as a siphon, a steam engine, a fire engine that pumped water, an altar fire that was mechanically lighted as soon as the temple doors were opened, a wind organ, a robot that poured wine, and mirrors possessing all sorts of bizarre properties. There was also Gerbert (ca. 950–1003), who became Pope Sylvester II and who constructed abaci, terrestrial and celestial globes, a clock, and perhaps an organ. Simon Stevin (1548–1620) astonished the citizens of his day with a sailwagon. John Napier (1550–1617) was the science fiction man of his age and previsioned, at least on paper, the modern machine gun, war tank, and submarine. Galileo (1564–1642) made telescopes, invented the first modern type microscope, and designed the once very popular sector compasses. William Oughtred (1574–1660) invented circular and straight slide rules. Blaise Pascal (1623–1662) constructed the world's first adding machines and invented the one-wheeled wheelbarrow. The great Dutch genius Christiaan Huygens (1629–1695) made clocks and watches. The youthful Isaac Newton (1642–1727) was remarkably inventive, making—among other things—

kites that carried lanterns, little grist mills run by mice, and toys for his friends. Gottfried Wilhelm Leibniz (1646–1716) invented a calculating machine that multiplied.

Another man of the same sort was Johann Müller (1436–1476), the ablest and most influential mathematician of the fifteen century, and more generally known, from the Latinized form of his birthplace of Königsberg ("king's mountain"), as Regiomontanus. At a young age he studied under Peuerbach in Vienna and was later entrusted with the task of completing the latter's translation of the *Almagest*. He also translated, from the Greek, works of Apollonius, Heron, and Archimedes. His treatise *De triangulis omnimodis*, written about 1464 but posthumously published in 1533, is his greatest mathematical achievement and was the first systematic European exposition of plane and spherical trigonometry considered independently of astronomy.

Regiomontanus traveled much in Italy and Germany, finally settling in 1471 at Nuremberg. It was there that he built an astronomical observatory and established a printing press. But the device that won him most admiration was a mechanical eagle that flapped its wings and saluted Emperor Maximilian I when that monarch entered Nuremberg. This mechanical eagle, which exhibited considerable mechanical ingenuity, was regarded as one of the marvels of the age.

In 1475, Regiomontanus was invited to Rome by Pope Sixtus IV to partake in the reformation of the calendar. Shortly after his arrival, at the age of 40, he suddenly died. Some mystery shrouds his death, for, though most accounts claim he probably died of a pestilence, it was rumored that he was poisoned by an enemy.

121° *Introduction of + and −.*   The first appearance in print of our present + and − signs was in an arithmetic, published in Leipzig in 1489, by Johannes Widman (born ca. 1460 in Bohemia). Here the signs are not used as symbols of operation but merely to indicate excess and deficiency. These signs were used in the same way in some slightly earlier written manuscripts that Widman had studied.

It may be that the plus sign is a contraction of the Latin word *et*, which was frequently used to indicate addition, and it may be that the minus sign is contracted from the abbreviation $\bar{m}$ for minus. Again, the minus sign may be the simple hyphen that was used by merchants to separate the indication of the weight of the receptacle from the total weight of the merchandise. Other more or less plausible explanations have been offered.

The + and − signs were used as symbols of algebraic operation in 1514 by the Dutch mathematician Van der Hoeke but were probably so used earlier.

122° *The cossic art.*   Many mathematicians of the fifteenth and sixteenth centuries, following the practice of Fibonacci and the Arabs, called the unknown quantity the *thing*—in Italian, *cosa*. It is for this reason that algebra was sometimes designated as the *cossic art*. For example, in 1525, Christoff Rudolff wrote an algebra entitled *Die Coss*. This algebra was very influential in Germany and an improved edition of it was brought out by Michael Stifel (1486–1567) in 1553. It was in Rudolff's book that our familiar radical sign (adopted perhaps because it resembles a small *r*, for *radix*) was introduced.

123° *Leonardo da Vinci's proof of the Pythagorean Theorem.*   There is a clever proof of the Pythagorean Theorem claimed to have been devised by the great artist Leonardo da Vinci (1452–1519). It is a congruency-by-subtraction proof, based on the diagram of Figure 20. Since, in that figure, the quadrilaterals *IFGH*, *IFBA*, *CJDA*, and *JCBE* are congruent, it follows that the hexagons *ABFGHI* and *ACBEJD* have equal areas. But hexagon *ABFGHI* is composed of the squares on the legs of the right triangle *ABC* along with two triangles congruent to triangle *ABC*; and hexagon *ACBEJD* is composed of the square on the hypotenuse of the right triangle *ABC* along with two triangles congruent to triangle *ABC*. It now follows that the sum of the squares on the legs of the right triangle *ABC* is equal to the square on the hypotenuse.

There is a work, *De diuina proportione*, of the Italian friar Luca Pacioli (ca. 1445–ca. 1509) that contains figures of the regular solids thought to have been drawn by Leonardo da Vinci. The book was published in 1509. Seldom is an author of a mathematical text able to secure such an outstanding artist to illustrate his work.

124° *The stone upon which one may sharpen his wits.*   The most influential British textbook writer of the sixteenth century was

Robert Recorde (ca. 1510–1558). Recorde wrote in English, his works appearing as dialogues between master and student. He studied at Oxford and then took a medical degree at Cambridge. He taught mathematics in private classes at both institutions while in residence there, and after leaving Cambridge he served as physician to Edward VI and Queen Mary.

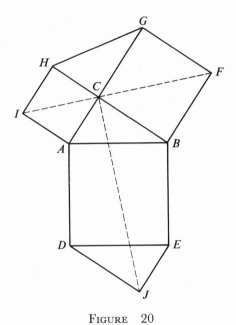

FIGURE 20

Recorde wrote at least four mathematical texts, each bearing a finely suggestive title: an arithmetic entitled *The Grovnd of Artes* (1542), which enjoyed at least 29 printings; an astronomy named *The Castle of Knowledge* (1551), which was one of the first works to introduce the Copernican system to English readers; a geometry called *The Pathewaie to Knowledge* (1551), which contained an abridgment of Euclid's *Elements*; and an algebra with the especially fine title of *The Whetstone of Witte* (1557), in which our modern symbol for equality was used for the first time.

On the title page of *The Whetstone of Witte* are two stanzas of verse, among which are the lines:

Here if you lift your wittes to whette,
Moche sharpenesse therby shall you gette.
Dulle wittes hereby doe greately mende,
Sharpe wittes are fined to their fulle ende.
Now proue, and praise, as you doe finde,
And to your self be not vnkinde.

125° *The origin of our equal sign.* Recorde justified his adoption of a pair of equal parallel line segments for the symbol of equality "bicause noe 2 thynges can be moare equalle." Of further interest here is a remark made by Recorde in his geometry work. There he says, "Parallels, or gemowe [i.e. twin] lynes be suche lines as be drawen foorth still in one distaunce, and are no nerer in one place then in an other, for if they be nerer at one ende then in the other, then are they no parallels." Thus the equality of the spaces between the two left ends and between the two right ends of the line segments of his equality symbol may also have influenced his choice of the symbol. Later, when the inequality symbols (> and <) were introduced by Thomas Harriot (1560–1621), that writer may have chosen his symbols because of the inequality of the spaces between the two left ends and between the two right ends of the involved line segments. (See Item 149°.)

126° *The death of Robert Recorde.* In later life Robert Recorde became "Comptroller of the Mines and Monies" in Ireland. His last years were spent in poor health in prison, and though for many years it was supposed he was imprisoned for personal debt, it now seems that he may have committed some misdemeanor in connection with his work in Ireland. Apparently he foresaw his end, for his algebra text, *The Whetstone of Witte*, closes with the lines:

Master. But harke, what meaneth that hastie knockyng at the doore?
Scholar. It is a messenger.
Master. What is the message; tel me in mine eare. Yea Sir is that the matter. Then is there noe remedie, but that I must neglect all studies and teaching, for to withstande those daungers. My fortune is not so good, to haue quiete tyme to teache. . . . I mighte haue been quietly permitted, to rest but a little lōger.

Robert Recorde died in the King's Bench Prison in 1558.

127° *Adam Riese.* With the interest in education that accompanied the Renaissance and with the tremendous increase in commercial activity at the time, hosts of popular textbooks in arithmetic began to appear. At least three hundred such books were printed in Europe prior to the seventeenth century. These texts were largely of two types, those written in Latin by classical scholars often attached to the Church schools, and those written in the vernaculars by practical teachers interested in preparing boys for commercial careers. These latter teachers often also served as town surveyors, notaries, and gaugers, and included the influential Rechenmeisters supported by the Hanseatic League, a powerful protective union of commercial towns in the Teutonic countries.

The greatest of all the Rechenmeisters of the sixteenth century was Adam Riese (1492–1559). As the most influential of the German writers of arithmetics, he was in Germany what Robert Recorde was in England. His commercial arithmetic published in 1522 ran through at least 37 editions before 1600. So reputable was this work that even today in Germany the phrase *nach Adam Riese* is used to indicate arithmetical skill and accuracy.

A cute geometrical story is told about Adam Riese. It seems that one day Riese and a draftsman entered into a friendly contest to see which one of them could, with straightedge and compasses, draw more right angles in one minute. The draftsman drew a straight line and then proceeded, by the standard method now taught in high school, to erect perpendiculars to the line. Adam Riese, on the other hand, drew a semicircle on a straight line and then in rapid order drew a large number of inscribed right angles. Riese easily won the contest.

128° *Nicolaus Copernicus.* There are a number of stories concerning efforts of a student on behalf of his teacher. Such a story is told of Georg Joachim Rhaeticus (1514–1576) and his former teacher Nicolaus Copernicus (1473–1543). Rhaeticus had once studied for two years under Copernicus and became an enthusiastic supporter of his teacher's heliocentric theory of the universe. If it hadn't been for the energetic importunities of Rhaeticus, Copernicus would never have seen his great work in print. It is said that the first copy off the press was rushed to Copernicus as he lay on his deathbed and that just before he lapsed into insensibility the copy was placed in the dying author's hands.

129° *Michael Stifel.* Michael Stifel (1486–1567) has been described as the greatest German algebraist of the sixteenth century. His best known mathematical work is his *Arithmetica integra*, published in 1544. In the first part of this work, Stifel points out the advantages of associating an arithmetical progression with a geometrical one, thus foreshadowing the invention of logarithms by John Napier nearly a century later.

Stifel was one of the oddest personalities in the history of mathematics. He was originally a monk, was converted by Martin Luther, and became a fanatical reformer. His erratic mind led him to indulge in number mysticism. From an analysis of Biblical writings, he prophesied the end of the world on October 3, 1533. He convinced a large number of believing peasants to abandon their work and property and to wait with him on the appointed day on a neighboring hilltop, where a chariot was to touch down and conduct him and his followers to heaven. Feeling a growing lack of confidence as the day progressed, Stifel excused himself from his worried believers for a moment, raced into town, and coaxed the local constabulary there to lock him safely in jail. His life was thus saved from the later bitter anger of the peasants whose lives he had ruined.

From this we learn that if you *must* predict the end of the world, be sure to select a date well beyond the end of your possible life span. This sage advice was followed in later years by John Napier (1550–1617), who claimed the Creator proposed to end the world some time in the years between 1688 and 1700.

130° *The art of beasting.* An extreme example of Stifel's mystical reasoning is his proof, by arithmology, that Pope Leo X was the "beast" mentioned in the *Book of Revelations*: "Let him that hath understanding count the number of the beast: for it is the number of a man; and his number is six hundred three score and six."

From LEO DECIMVS, Stifel retained L, D, C, I, M, V, since these letters have significance in the Roman numeral system. He then added X, for Leo X and because *Leo decimvs* contains ten letters, and omitted the M, because it stands for *mysterium*. A rearrangement of the letters gave DCLXVI, or 666, the "number of the beast" in the *Book of Revelations*. This discovery gave Stifel such extreme comfort that he believed his interpretation must have resulted from an inspiration from God.

Some years later, Napier, the inventor of logarithms, showed that 666 stands for the Pope at Rome, and his Jesuit contemporary, Father Bongus, declared that it stands for Martin Luther. Father Bongus's reasoning ran as follows. If from A to I represents 1 to 9, from K to S represents 10 to 90 (by tens), and T to Z represents 100 to 500 (by hundreds),* we obtain

M	A	R	T	I	N		L	V	T	E	R	A
30	1	80	100	9	40		20	200	100	5	80	1

which gives, as a sum, 666.

During World War I, arithmology was used to show that 666 must be interpreted as Kaiser Wilhelm. It has been shown that 666 spells Nero when expressed in the letter symbols of the Aramaic language in which the *Book of Revelations* was originally written.

Augustus De Morgan said that when it comes to the use of interpretations of one branch of the Church against another, the true explanation of the three sixes is that the interpreters are "six of one and half a dozen of the other."

THE EPISODE OF CUBIC AND QUARTIC EQUATIONS

SOME cubic equations are found on ancient Babylonian tablets, and Archimedes cleverly solved a cubic equation that arose in his work *On the Sphere and Cylinder*. Also, Omar Khayyam solved cubic equations geometrically insofar as the positive roots are concerned. But it was the Italian algebraists of the sixteenth century who first solved general cubic and quartic equations in terms of the coefficients of the equations. The story of this discovery, when told in its most colorful version, rivals any pages ever written by Benvenuto Cellini.

---

* The Latin alphabet is like the English, except that it lacks j and w. Moreover, in the upper-case letters, a U appears as a V.

131° *The story of the algebraic solution of cubic equations.*   Briefly told, the facts seem to be these. About 1515, Scipione del Ferro (1465–1526), a professor of mathematics at the University of Bologna, solved algebraically the cubic equation $x^3 + mx = n$, probably basing his work on earlier Arabic sources. He did not publish his result but revealed the secret to his pupil Antonio Fior. Now about 1535, Nicolo of Brescia, commonly referred to as Tartaglia ("the stammerer") because of a childhood injury which affected his speech, claimed to have discovered an algebraic solution of the cubic equation $x^3 + px^2 = n$. Believing this claim was a bluff, Fior challenged Tartaglia to a public contest of solving cubic equations, whereupon the latter exerted himself and only a few days before the contest found an algebraic solution for cubics lacking a quadratic term. Entering the contest equipped to solve two types of cubic equations, whereas Fior could solve but one type, Tartaglia triumphed completely. Later Girolamo Cardano, an unprincipled genius who taught mathematics and practiced medicine in Milan, upon giving a solemn pledge of secrecy, wheedled the key to the cubic from Tartaglia. In 1545, Cardano published his *Ars magna*, a great Latin treatise on algebra, at Nuremberg, Germany, and in it appeared Tartaglia's solution of the cubic. Tartaglia's vehement protests were met by Lodovico Ferrari, Cardano's most capable pupil, who argued that Cardano had received his information from del Ferro through a third party and accused Tartaglia of plagiarism from the same source. There ensued an acrimonious dispute from which Tartaglia was perhaps lucky to escape alive.

Since some of the actors in the above drama seem not always to have had the highest regard for truth, one finds a number of variations in the details of the plot.

132° *Girolamo Cardano.*   Girolamo Cardano is one of the most extraordinary characters in the history of mathematics. He was born in Pavia in 1501 as the illegitimate son of a jurist and developed into a man of passionate contrasts. He commenced his turbulent professional life as a doctor, studying, teaching, and writing mathematics while practicing his profession. He once traveled as far as Scotland and upon his return to Italy successively held important chairs at the Universities of Pavia and Bologna. He was imprisoned for a time for heresy because he published a horoscope of Christ's life, showing that whatever Christ did he had to by the dictation of his stars. Resigning his chair in Bologna he moved to Rome and became a distinguished astrologer, receiving, oddly enough, a pension as astrologer to the papal court. He died in Rome in 1576, by drinking poison, one story says, so as to fulfill his earlier astrological prediction of the date of his death. Many stories are told of his wickedness, as when in a fit of rage he cut off the ears of his younger son. At about the same time, his older son was executed for murder. An inveterate gambler, Cardano wrote a gambler's manual in which are considered some interesting questions on probability. It may be that history has somewhat maligned Cardano. Cardano's autobiography, of course, supports this view.

133° *Tartaglia.*   Tartaglia had a hard childhood. He was born about 1499 at Brescia to very poor parents. He was present at the taking of Brescia in 1512 by the French. After the capture of the town, most of the inhabitants sought sanctuary in the cathedral, but were there massacred by the soldiers. Tartaglia's father, who was a postal messenger of the town, was among those who were killed. The boy suffered some severe saber cuts that split his skull in three places and cleft his jaws and palate. He was left for dead, but when his mother, who had hidden elsewhere, got to the cathedral to search out her family, she found him still alive and managed to carry him off. Lacking all resources she recalled that a dog when wounded always licks the injured place. So for days she licked the poor boy's head. He ultimately recovered, but the injury to his palate left him with an impediment in his speech, and it was from this that he received his nickname of Tartaglia, the stammerer.

It was only with great sacrifice that the boy was able to educate himself. His mother scraped together sufficient money to send him to school for fifteen days, along with the advice that he must make the best of his opportunity. This he interpreted by stealing a copybook from which he later taught himself how to read and write. It is said that lacking the means to buy paper, he was obliged to use the tombstones in the cemetery as slates.

Tartaglia later earned his livelihood teaching science and mathematics in various Italian cities. He was a gifted mathematician. In addition to his success in solving cubic equations, he is credited with being the first to apply mathematics to the science of artillery fire. He wrote what is generally considered the best Italian arithmetic of the sixteenth century, and he published editions of Euclid and Archimedes. He died in Venice in 1557.

134° *The story of the algebraic solution of quartic equations.* It was not long after the cubic had been solved that an algebraic solution was discovered for the general quartic equation. In 1540, the Italian mathematician Zuanne da Coi proposed the following problem to Cardano: "Divide 10 into three parts such that they shall be in continued proportion and that the product of the first two shall be 6." If the three parts be denoted by a, b, c, we have

$$a + b + c = 10, \quad ac = b^2, \quad ab = 6.$$

If a and c are eliminated we obtain the quartic equation

$$b^4 + 6b^2 + 36 = 60b.$$

Although Cardano was unable to solve the equation, his pupil Ferrari succeeded, and Cardano had the pleasure of publishing this solution, as well as Tartaglia's solution of the cubic, in his *Ars magna*.

FRANÇOIS VIÈTE

THE greatest French mathematician of the sixteenth century was François Viète, frequently called by his semi-Latin name of Vieta, a lawyer and member of parliament who devoted most of his leisure time to mathematics. He wrote a number of works on trigonometry, algebra, and geometry, most of which were printed and distributed at his own expense. He was born in 1540 at Fontenay and died in 1603 in Paris.

135° *The origin of a friendship.* Some entertaining anecdotes are told about Viète. Thus there is the story about the ambassador from the Low Countries who boasted to King Henry IV that France had no mathematician capable of solving a problem proposed in 1593 by his countryman Adrianus Romanus (1561–1615) and which required the solution of a 45th degree equation. Viète was summoned and shown the equation. Recognizing an underlying trigonometric connection he was able, in a few minutes, to give two roots, and then later gave twenty-one more. The negative roots escaped him. In return Viète challenged Romanus to solve the problem of Apollonius (to draw a circle tangent to three given circles), but Romanus was unable to obtain a solution using Euclidean tools. When he was shown the proposer's elegant solution he traveled to Fontenay to meet Viète with the result that a warm friendship developed.

136° *Christian versus unchristian.*   There is also the story of how Viète successfully deciphered a Spanish code containing several hundred characters and for two years France profited thereby in its war with Spain. So certain was King Philip II that the code was un-decipherable that he complained to the Pope that the French were employing magic against his country, "contrary to the practice of the Christian faith." We note that there was no complaint that the war was contrary to the practice of the Christian faith.

137° *Work unfit for a Christian.*   In his *De numerosa potestatum resolutione* of 1600, Viète gives a systematic process for successively approximating to a root of an algebraic equation. Though the method was in general use until about 1680, the procedure becomes so laborious for equations of high degree that one seventeenth-century mathematician described it as "work unfit for a Christian."

SIMON STEVIN, JOHN NAPIER, AND HENRY BRIGGS

MANY of the fields in which numerical calculations are important, such as astronomy, navigation, trade, engineering, and war, have made ever increasing demands that these computations be performed more quickly and accurately. These increasing demands were met successively by four remarkable inventions: the Hindu-Arabic notation, decimal fractions, logarithms, and the modern computing machines. The earliest systematic treatment of the second of these devices was given by Simon Stevin in his influential text on arithmetic of 1585 entitled *La Disme*. The third of the great labor-saving devices was the invention of John Napier and appeared in his brochure of 1615 entitled *Mirifici logarithmorum canonis descriptio* (A Description of the Wonderful Law of Logarithms). Henry Briggs helped to perfect Napier's invention and devoted great energies toward the construction of the first table of common logarithms.

Simon Stevin was born at Bruges in 1548. In later life he served as quartermaster general of the Dutch Army and directed many public works. He was the most influential mathematician of the Low Countries in the sixteenth century and he won a high reputation for his work on statics and hydrostatics. He died at the Hague in 1620.

John Napier, who was born in 1550 when his father was only sixteen years of age, lived most of his life at the imposing family estate of Merchiston Castle, near Edinburgh, Scotland, and expended most of his energies in the political and religious controversies of his day. He was violently anti-Catholic and championed the causes of John Knox and James I. As relaxation from his political and religious polemics, Napier amused himself with the study of mathematics and science. He died in 1617.

Henry Briggs was born near Halifax, England, in 1561. He had the honor of being the first occupant of a chair of geometry founded by Sir Thomas Gresham in 1596 at Gresham College in London and the first occupant of a chair of geometry founded by Sir Henry Savile in 1619 at Oxford University. Briggs died at Oxford in 1631.

138° *A multiple reputation.* In the history of mathematics, Stevin is best known as one of the earliest expositors of the theory of decimal fractions. In the history of physics he is best known for his contributions to statics and hydrostatics. To the savants of his time he was best known for his works on fortifications and military engineering. To the general populace of his time he was best known for his invention of a carriage propelled by sails, which ran along the seashore carrying 28 people and easily outstripping a galloping horse.

139° *Napier's misjudgment of himself.* In 1593, Napier published a bitter and widely read attack on the Church of Rome entitled *A Plaine Discouery of the whole Reuelation of Saint Iohn*, in which he endeavored to prove that the Pope was Anti-Christ and that the Creator proposed to end the world in the years between 1688 and 1700. The book ran through twenty-one editions, at least ten of them during the author's lifetime. Napier sincerely believed that his reputation with posterity would rest upon this book. How wrong he proved to be! His book is today totally disregarded and known only to a curious few. Instead, his reputation today rests solidly, widely, and almost solely upon one of his mathematical diversions, the invention of logarithms.

140° *The science fiction writer of his day.* Napier wrote prophetically of various infernal war engines, accompanying his writings with plans and diagrams. He predicted the future would develop a piece of artillery that could "clear a field of four miles circumference of all living creatures exceeding a foot of height," that it would produce "devices for sayling under water," and that it would create a chariot with "a living mouth of mettle" that would "scatter destruction on all sides." In World War I these were realized as the machine gun, the submarine, and the army tank, respectively.

141° *Exposing a thief.* It is no wonder that Napier's remarkable ingenuity and imagination led some to believe he was mentally unbalanced and others to regard him as a dealer in the black art. Many stories, probably unfounded, are told in support of these views. Thus there was the time he announced that his coal black rooster would identify to him which one of his servants was stealing from him. He put his rooster in a box in a darkened room and instructed the servants to enter one by one and to place a hand on the rooster's back. Napier assured his servants that his rooster would expose the culprit to him at the completion of these performances. Now, unknown to the servants, Napier had coated the bird's back with lampblack. The innocent servants, having nothing to fear, did as they were bidden, but the guilty one decided to protect himself by not touching the bird. In this way he was exposed, for he was the only servant to return from the darkened room with clean hands.

142° *Impounding pigeons.* Napier was annoyed by a neighbor's pigeons that flew onto his land and ate his grain. He accordingly asked the neighbor to restrict the pigeons' flights, otherwise he would have to impound the birds as payment for the stolen grain. The neighbor, believing the capture of his pigeons to be virtually impossible, said that Napier was welcome to the birds if he could catch them. Imagine the neighbor's surprise when next day he observed his pigeons staggering and reeling on Napier's lawn and Napier calmly going about collecting them and putting them into a large sack. Napier had soaked some peas in wine or brandy and scattered them about his lawn. He then found it easy to collect the drunk birds and put them in the sack.

143° *The meeting.* Briggs so admired Napier's invention of logarithms that he decided to travel from London to Edinburgh to meet the ingenious Scotsman. Briggs was delayed on the journey and the awaiting Napier complained to a common friend, "Ah, John, Mr. Briggs will not come." At that very moment a knock was heard at the gate and Briggs was ushered into Napier's presence. For almost a quarter of an hour each man beheld the other without speaking a word. Then Briggs said, "My lord, I have undertaken this long journey purposely to see your person, and to know by what engine of wit or ingenuity you came first to think of this most excellent help in astronomy, namely, the logarithms, but, my lord, being by you found out, I wonder nobody found it out before, when now known it is so easy." Briggs remained at Merchiston Castle for a month as Napier's guest.

144° *Some terminology.* The word *logarithm* means "ratio number," and was adopted by Napier after first using the expression *artificial number.* Briggs introduced the word *mantissa* (for the decimal part of a logarithm), which is a late Latin term of Etruscan origin, originally meaning an "addition" or "makeweight," and which in the sixteenth century came to mean "appendix." The term *characteristic* (for the integral part of a logarithm) was also suggested by Briggs and used by Adriaen Vlacq (1600–1666), a Dutch bookseller and publisher who helped complete the table of logarithms started by Briggs. It is curious that it was customary in early tables of common logarithms to print the characteristic as well as the mantissa, and that it was not until the eighteenth century that the present custom of printing only the mantissa was established.

145° *Laplace's statement.* Napier's wonderful invention of logarithms was enthusiastically adopted throughout Europe. In astronomy, in particular, the time was overripe for such a discovery. As Pierre-Simon Laplace (1749–1827) once asserted, the invention of logarithms "by shortening the labors doubled the life of the astronomer."

146° *A historical curiosity.* Nowadays a logarithm is universally regarded as an exponent. Thus if $n = b^x$, we say x is the logarithm of n to the base b. From this definition the laws of logarithms follow immediately from the laws of exponents. One of the curiosities of the history of mathematics is the fact that logarithms were discovered before exponents were in use.

147° *Napierian logarithms versus natural logarithms.* As we know today, the power of logarithms as a computing device lies in the fact that by them multiplication and division are reduced to the simpler operations of addition and subtraction. A forerunner of this idea is apparent in the formula

$$\sin A \sin B = \tfrac{1}{2}[\cos (A - B) - \cos (A + B)],$$

well known in Napier's time, and it is quite probable that Napier's line of thought started with this formula, since otherwise it is difficult to account for his initial restriction of logarithms to those of the sines of angles. Napier labored at least twenty years upon his theory, and, whatever the genesis of his idea, his final definition of a logarithm is as follows. Consider a line segment AB and an infinite ray DE, as shown in Figure 21. Let points C and F start moving simultaneously from A and D, respectively, along these lines, with the same initial rate. Suppose C moves with a velocity always numerically equal to the

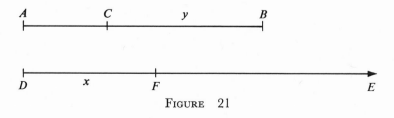

F I G U R E   21

distance CB, and that F moves with a uniform velocity. Then Napier defined DF to be the logarithm of CB. That is, setting $DF = x$ and $CB = y$,

$$x = \text{Nap log } y.$$

In order to avoid the nuisance of fractions, Napier took the length of AB as 10^7, for the best tables of sines available to him extended to seven places. From Napier's definition, and through the use of knowledge not available to Napier, it develops that*

$$\text{Nap log } y = 10^7 \log_{1/e} (y/10^7),$$

so that the frequently made statement that Napierian logarithms are natural logarithms is actually without basis. One observes that the Napierian logarithm decreases as the number increases, contrary to what happens with natural logarithms.

It further develops that, over a succession of equal periods of time, y *decreases* in *geometric* progression while x *increases* in *arithmetic* progression. Thus we have the fundamental principle of a system of logarithms, the association of a geometric and an arithmetic progression. It now follows, for example, that if $a/b = c/d$, then

$$\text{Nap log } a - \text{Nap log } b = \text{Nap log } c - \text{Nap log } d,$$

which is one of the many results established by Napier.

It was when Briggs visited Napier that both men agreed that the tables would be more useful if they were altered so that the logarithm of 1 would be 0 and the logarithm of 10 would be an appropriate

---

* The result is easily shown with the aid of a little calculus. Thus we have $AC = 10^7 - y$, whence velocity of $C = -dy/dt = y$. That is, $dy/y = -dt$, or integrating, $\ln y = -t + C$. Evaluating the constant of integration by substituting $t = 0$, we find $C = \ln 10^7$, whence

$$\ln y = -t + \ln 10^7.$$

Now

$$\text{velocity of } F = dx/dt = 10^7,$$

so that $x = 10^7 t$. Therefore

$$\text{Nap log } y = x = 10^7 t = 10^7 (\ln 10^7 - \ln y)$$
$$= 10^7 \ln (10^7/y) = 10^7 \log_{1/e} (y/10^7).$$

power of 10. Thus were born the so-called *Briggsian,* or *common,* logarithms of today. Logarithms of this sort, which are essentially logarithms to the base 10, owe their superior utility in numerical computations to the fact that our number system also is based on 10. For a number system having some other base *b* it would, of course, be most convenient for computational purposes to have tables of logarithms also to the base *b*.

THOMAS HARRIOT AND WILLIAM OUGHTRED

THOMAS Harriot (1560–1621) is usually considered the founder of the English school of algebraists. His great work in this field, the *Artis analyticae praxis,* was not published until ten years after his death. This work did much toward setting the present standards for a textbook on the theory of equations. William Oughtred (1574–1660) was one of the most influential of the seventeenth-century English writers on mathematics. In the same year, 1631, that Harriot's work on algebra appeared, there also appeared the first edition of Oughtred's popular *Clavis mathematicae,* a work on arithmetic and algebra that did much toward spreading mathematical knowledge in England. Oughtred placed emphasis on mathematical symbols, giving over 150 of them, of which only three have come down to present times: the cross (×) for multiplication, the four dots (::) used in a proportion, and our frequently used symbol for "difference between" (~).

148° *Harriot in America.* Thomas Harriot is of special interest to Americans because in 1585 he was sent by Sir Walter Raleigh as a surveyor with Sir Richard Greenville's expedition to the New World to map what was then called Virginia but is now North Carolina.

149° *On the origin of > and <.* During his stay of roughly a year in America, Harriot took the opportunity to study the Indians and to learn to speak their language. Upon returning to England, he wrote a book entitled *A Brief and True Report of the New Found Land of Virginia, of the Commodities, and of the Nature and Manner of the Naturall Inhabitants* (first edition 1588, second edition 1590). Captain John

White, who accompanied Harriot, made sketches of scenes and people seen by the two men. In the 1590 edition of Harriot's book appeared engravings made by Thomas de Bry of some of the sketches drawn by White. One of these engravings shows a rear view of an Indian chief on whose left shoulder blade appears the mark reproduced in Figure 22. If the small serif-like marks are removed, and the resulting symbol

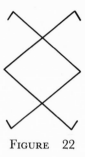

FIGURE   22

pulled apart in the horizontal direction, there will appear two symbols similar to those that Harriot chose for "is greater than" and "is less than." It is thus possible, as was pointed out by Charles L. Smith of the State University of New York at Potsdam, that a mark on the back of an Indian chief suggested to Harriot two mathematical symbols that have now been in use for more than three centuries.

In the absence of any stated or recorded motivation on the part of Harriot, the above explanation could well be the true one. But there is at least one feature of Harriot's early symbols perhaps militating against the conjecture. Harriot constructed his inequality signs as very long, horizontally drawn-out symbols, and not at all like the short stubby symbols appearing on the Indian chief's back.

Of course, since Harriot had adopted the long drawn-out equality sign of Robert Recorde, it could be that his long drawn-out inequality signs were so designed merely for similitude of representation. However, one would like to think that Harriot had a more rational motivation for the origin of his symbols than an adaptation of marks appearing on the back of an Indian chief. Such a rational and easily conceived motivation would be this: In an expression like $2 = 2$, the space between the two left ends of the bars of the equality sign is equal to the space between the two right ends of these bars, and, also, the number on the left of the equality sign is equal to the number on the right. Therefore, in designing a symbol to represent the qualitative relation between 4 and 2, say, since the left number 4 is greater than the right number 2, why not adopt a symbol composed of two *converging* bars, so that the space between the two left ends of these bars is greater than that between the two right ends of the bars? Because of Harriot's adoption of the long equality sign, a long inequality sign for "is greater than," composed of two converging bars like we have just described, should, to circumvent possible misinterpretation, *completely* converge, yielding, over the years, $4 > 2$.

Whatever Harriot's motivation might have been for the origin of his inequality signs, the motivation described immediately above has fine pedagogical value, and once a student hears this motivation he will never confound the two symbols $>$ and $<$.

150° *The teacher of giants.* Oughtred was, by profession, an Episcopal minister. He is reputed to have been a "pittiful preacher," but his sermons rapidly improved when the gathering Puritan Revolution shrank his congregation and threatened his livelihood. He preferred to work at mathematics and gave free private lessons to pupils interested in the subject. Among his pupils were John Wallis, Christopher Wren, and Seth Ward, later famous, respectively, as a mathematician, an architect, and an astronomer.

151° *The invention of the slide rule.* In his work *The Circles of Proportion* (1632), Oughtred described a circular slide rule. He was not, however, the first to describe in print a slide rule of the circular type, and an argument of priority of invention rests between him and Richard Delamain, one of his pupils. But Oughtred does seem unquestionably to have invented, about 1622, the straight logarithmic slide rule. In 1620, Edmund Gunter (1581–1626) constructed a logarithmic scale, or a line of numbers on which the distances are proportional to the logarithms of the numbers indicated, and mechanically performed multiplications and divisions by adding and subtracting segments of this scale with the aid of a pair of dividers. The idea of carrying out these additions and subtractions by having two like logarithmic scales, one sliding along the other as shown in Figure

FIGURE   23

23, is due to Oughtred. Although Oughtred invented such a simple slide rule as early as 1622, he did not describe it in print until 1632. A runner for the slide rule was suggested by Isaac Newton in 1675, but was not actually constructed until nearly a century later. Several slide rules for special purposes, such as for commercial transactions, for measuring timber, and so forth, were devised in the seventeenth century. The log log scale was invented in 1815, and it was in 1850 that the French army officer Amédée Mannheim (1831–1906) standardized the modern sliding rule.

152° *Oughtred's longevity.* In speaking of his college days, Oughtred said:

> The time which over and above those usuall studies I employed upon the Mathematical sciences, I redeemed night by night from my naturall sleep, defrauding my body, and inuring it to watching, cold, and labour, while most others tooke their rest.

And Aubrey, in his *Brief Lives*, gives this description of Oughtred:

> He was a little man, had black haire, and blacke eies (with a great deal of spirit). His head was always working. He would drawe lines and diagrams in the dust . . . did use to lye a bed till eleaven or twelve a clock . . . Studied late at night; went not to bed till 11 a clock; had his tinder box by him; and on the top of his bed-staffe, he had his inke-horne fix't. He slept but little. Sometimes he went not to bed in two or three nights.

Oughtred thus seems to have ignored the usual rules of good health, and probably continued to ignore them throughout his long life. When he finally died, it is said that he did so in a transport of joy at receiving the news of the restoration of Charles II. To this Augustus De Morgan once remarked, "It should be added, by way of excuse, that he was eighty-six years old."

GALILEO GALILEI AND JOHANNES KEPLER

THERE were two outstanding astronomers who contributed notably to mathematics in the early part of the seventeenth century, the Italian, Galileo Galilei (1564–1642), and the German, Johannes Kepler (1571–1630). To Galileo we owe the modern spirit of science as a harmony between experiment and theory. He founded the mechanics of freely falling bodies and laid the foundation of dynamics in general, a foundation upon which Isaac Newton was able later to build the science. To Kepler we owe one of the most remarkable inductions in science, his famous three laws of planetary motion, arrived at after extraordinary pertinacity and after much computational labor, trial and error, and false solutions. These laws of planetary motion are landmarks in the history of astronomy and mathematics, for in an effort to justify them Isaac Newton was led to create modern celestial mechanics.

153° *The oscillating lamp.*   At the age of seventeen, Galileo was sent by his parents to the University of Pisa to study medicine. One day, while attending a service in the cathedral at Pisa, his mind was distracted by a great bronze lamp which was suspended from the ceiling and which oscillated to and fro with changing amplitude. Using the beat of his pulse to keep time, he was surprised to find that the period of an oscillation of the lamp was independent of the size of the arc of oscillation. By experiments, he later showed that the period of a swinging pendulum is also independent of the weight of the pendulum's bob, and thus depends solely on the length of the pendulum. It is said that Galileo's interest in science and mathematics was roused by this problem, and then further stimulated by the chance attendance at a lecture on mathematics at the University. The result was that he asked for, and secured, parental permission to abandon medicine and to devote himself to science and mathematics instead, fields in which he possessed strong natural talent.

154° *Falling bodies.*   When Galileo was twenty-five, he received an appointment as professor of mathematics at the University of Pisa. It was while holding this appointment that he made his famous public experiments with falling bodies. Before a crowd of students, faculty, and priests, he dropped two pieces of metal, one ten times the weight of the other, from the top of the leaning tower of Pisa. The two pieces of metal struck the ground at practically the same moment, thus contradicting Aristotle, who said that a heavier body falls faster than a lighter one. But even the visual evidence of Galileo's experiment did not shake the faith of the other professors at the University in the teaching of Aristotle. The authorities at the University were so shocked at Galileo's sacrilegious insolence in contradicting Aristotle that they made life unpleasant for him there, with the result that in 1591 he resigned his professorship. The following year he accepted a professorship at the University of Padua, where there was an atmosphere more friendly to scientific pursuits. Here, for nearly eighteen years, Galileo continued his experiments and his teaching, and won widespread fame.

155° *The telescope, and further trouble.* About 1607, an apprentice to the spectacle maker, Hans Lippershay of Holland, while playing with some of his master's spectacle lenses, discovered that if he held two of the lenses at an appropriate distance apart, objects seen through the pair of lenses became enlarged. The apprentice brought his discovery to the attention of his master, who placed two lenses in a tube and displayed the device as a toy in his shop window. The toy was seen by a government official, who bought it and presented it to Prince Maurice of Nassau. As commander of the armed forces of the United Netherlands, Prince Maurice saw the possibilities of the toy as a spyglass for military use.

By 1609, news of the invention of the spyglass reached Galileo, who soon made a spyglass greatly superior to the one made by Lippershay. Upon request, he demonstrated his instrument in Venice, where, from the top of the highest church in the city, Venetian senators were able to see the sails of an approaching ship a full two hours before they were visible by naked eye. Galileo presented his model to the Doge of Venice, who, like Prince Maurice, recognized the immense possibilities of the instrument in naval and military operations, and Galileo was given a sizably increased stipend.

Galileo went on and made four more telescopes, as his instruments were named (from the Greek *tele*, "far," *skopos*, "watching"), each more powerful than the last. With the fifth telescope, which had a power of thirty diameters, Galileo noticed, on the night of January 7, 1610, two small stars to the east of the planet Jupiter and one to the west. The following night, to his surprise, all three stars were to the west of the planet, and three nights later he found there was still another small star revolving about Jupiter. He had discovered Jupiter's four bright satellites and was furnished a striking confirmation of the Copernican theory of smaller bodies revolving about larger ones. But this discovery only aroused once more the bigoted opposition of many churchmen, who accepted the authority of Aristotle; Aristotle had asserted that the earth, and hence man, is the center of the universe. One churchman even accused Galileo of placing the four satellites of Jupiter inside his telescope!

When Galileo named the four satellites "the Medicean stars," after the family name of the ruler of Tuscany, the Grand Duke of Tuscany was flattered and offered Galileo a munificent sinecure. Galileo accepted the offer and unwisely left the relatively free atmosphere of Venetia for the orthodox closeness of Tuscany.

At Florence, with the aid of his telescope, Galileo made further discoveries that confirmed the Copernican theory. He also discovered the existence of sunspots, which again contradicted Aristotle who claimed the sun is spotless and without blemish. Trouble was again brewing for Galileo. Copernicus's book was placed on the Index of prohibited works, there to remain for two hundred years, and Galileo was advised to cease upholding the Copernican theory. Nevertheless, in 1632, Galileo published his findings and his confirmation of the Copernican theory in his famous work which has come to be briefly referred to as the *Discorsi*.

156° *The inquisition and the unhappy end of a great scholar.* Not all churchmen were against Galileo and his discoveries. There were some more enlightened men, like Pope Gregory XV and Cardinal Barberini, who later became Pope, who did not oppose his views. In fact, Cardinal Barberini actually confirmed some of Galileo's discoveries by observing them through the telescope. Nevertheless, the forces of reaction gained the upper hand. By 1632, when Galileo published his famous *Discorsi*, in which the Copernican theory appears to triumph over the Ptolemaic theory, Cardinal Barberini had become Pope Urban VIII and now paid heed to the reactionaries who suggested that the character Simplicius ("the simpleton") in Galileo's book represented him as supporter of the Aristotelian-held Ptolemaic theory of the universe. The sale of Galileo's book was prohibited and a commission was appointed to look into the matter. The report was unfavorable and condemned Galileo for "maintaining that the earth moves and that the sun is stationary." Galileo was arrested and summoned before the Inquisition. On June 22, 1633, an ill and an old man, he was forced, under threat of torture, to declare, "I adjure, curse, and detest the said errors and heresies and generally every error and sect contrary to the said Holy Church; and I swear that I will nevermore in future say or assent anything verbally or in writing which may give rise to a similar suspicion of me; but that if I know any heretic, or any one suspected of heresy, I will denounce him to this Holy Office or to the Inquisitor and Ordinary of the place in which I may be."

Having thus perjured his conscience, the old scholar's life was broken. He was permitted to continue innocuous scientific work, but became blind and died in January, 1642, still under the supervision of the Inquisition and a virtual prisoner in his own home.

There is a legend that, as Galileo rose to his feet after his forced recantation and denial of the earth's motion, he muttered softly under his breath to himself, "The earth *does* move all the same." Whatever the basis of this story, it has come to be a sort of proverb to the effect that truth shall prevail despite all attempts at suppression. And so it came to pass, for the year 1642, which saw the death of Galileo in captivity, saw also the birth of Isaac Newton.

157° *Authority versus reasoning in science.* Galileo has been quoted as saying: "In questions of sciences, the authority of a thousand is not worth the humble reasoning of a single individual."

158° *Galileo's reconciliation of science and Scripture.* All his life long, Galileo was a religious man and a devout Catholic. It accordingly distressed him to find the views to which he was irresistibly led by his observations and reasonings as a scientist condemned as contradicting the Scriptures of the Church of which he considered himself a loyal member. He therefore felt impelled to think out for himself the relation between science and Scripture. Many Christian scientists have, from time to time, found themselves in this position. It occurred, for example, in the middle of the nineteenth century when difficulties were felt in reconciling Darwin's theory of evolution with the Biblical account of the creation of living things.

Galileo's conclusion was that the Bible is not, and never was intended to be, a textbook on astronomy, or biology, or any other science. In short, it was not intended as a book to teach us scientific truths that we can discover for ourselves. Rather, it was intended as a book to reveal spiritual truths that we could not have found out for ourselves. Now the conflict between science and Scripture lies in the fact that these spiritual truths are expressed in the Bible in ways natural to the people to whom, and through whom, they were originally revealed. But this is clearly just an accident of time and should therefore be overlooked. A scientist should not be upset to find the Bible picturing the world in a way natural to the early Hebrews, and a churchman should not be upset to find a scientist picturing the world in a way contrary to the description in the Bible. The way in which the world is described is entirely incidental to the real aim of the Bible, and no way is inconsistent with the spiritual teachings of the Bible.

159° *Some Galileo–Kepler correspondence.* When Kepler's work *Mysterium cosmographicum*, which openly advocated the Copernican theory, was published in 1596, the author sent a copy to Galileo. On August 4, 1597, Galileo wrote to Kepler thanking him for the book:

> I would certainly dare to approach the public with my ways of thinking if there were more people of your mind. As this is not the case, I shall refrain from doing so . . . .
>
> Yours in sincere friendship,
> GALILACUS GALILAEUS
> *Mathematician at the Academy of Padua*

A couple of months later, on October 13, 1597, Kepler replied to Galileo urging his fellow Copernican to be bold and proceed openly with his beliefs:

Be of good cheer, Galileo, and appear in public. If I am not mistaken, there are only a few among the distinguished mathematicians of Europe who would disassociate themselves from us . . . .

But, as we have seen in Item 156°, Galileo chose a later day for his day of reckoning.

160° *Tycho Brahe's golden nose.* In 1600 Kepler became associated with the eminent Danish-Swedish astronomer Tycho Brahe (1546–1601) as that man's assistant. Brahe was a hard man to work for as he was a vitriolic fellow of violent temper.

Some people have a glass eye, or a wooden leg; Brahe had a golden nose. Earlier in life, when he was located at the University of Rostock, a quarrel he had with a Danish nobleman led to a duel in which Brahe had the misfortune to lose a sizable piece of his nose. Brahe had the lost portion replaced by a piece of material composed of wax, silver, and gold.

When Brahe suddenly died in October, 1601, Kepler inherited both his master's position and his vast and very accurate collection of astronomical data on the motion of the planets.

161° *Kepler's pertinacity.* It has often been said that almost any problem can be solved if one but continuously worries over it and works at it a sufficiently long time. Somewhat as Thomas Edison said of invention being one percent inspiration and ninety-nine percent perspiration, problem solving is one percent imagination and ninety-nine percent perseverance. Perhaps nowhere in the history of science is this more clearly demonstrated than in Kepler's incredible pertinacity in solving the problem of the motion of the planets about the sun. Thoroughly convinced of the Copernican theory that the planets revolve in orbits about the central sun, Kepler strenuously sought to determine the nature and position of those orbits, and the manner in which the planets travel in their orbits. After many highly imaginative attempts (see, for example, Item 64°), made when he had little data to aid in verification, Kepler inherited Tycho Brahe's enormous mass of very accurate observations of the motion of the planets. The problem then became this: to obtain a pattern of motion of the planets that would exactly jibe with Brahe's great set of observations. So dependable were Brahe's recordings that any solution that should differ from Brahe's observed positions by even so little as a quarter of the moon's apparent diameter must be discarded as incorrect. Kepler had, then, first to guess with his *imagination* some plausible solution, and then with painful *perseverance* to endure the mountains of tedious calculation needed to confirm or reject his guess. He made hundreds of fruitless attempts and performed reams and reams of calculations, laboring with undiminished zeal and patience for twenty-two years. Finally he solved his problem, in the form of his three famous laws of planetary motion:

I. *The planets move about the sun in elliptical orbits with the sun at one focus.*

II. *The radius vector joining a planet to the sun sweeps over equal areas in equal intervals of time.*

III. *The square of the time of one complete revolution of a planet about its orbit is proportional to the cube of the orbit's semimajor axis.*

The empirical discovery of these laws from Brahe's mass of data constitutes one of the most remarkable inductions ever made in science. With justifiable pride, Kepler prefaced his *Harmony of the Worlds* of 1619 with the following poetic outburst:

I am writing a book for my contemporaries or—it does not matter—for posterity. It may be that my book will wait for a hundred years for a reader. Has not God waited for 6000 years for an observer?

162° *The rarity of problem solvers.* One now sees why there are so few expert problem solvers. An expert problem solver must be endowed with two incompatible qualities, a restless imagination and a patient pertinacity.

163° *Pure versus applied mathematics.* One never knows when a piece of pure mathematics may receive an unexpected application. As William Whewell once said, "If the Greeks had not cultivated the conic sections, Kepler could not have superseded Ptolemy." It is very interesting that 1800 years after the Greeks had developed the properties of the conics merely to satisfy their intellectual cravings, there should occur such an illuminating practical application of them.

164° *A life of misfortune.*   It is sad that Kepler's personal life was made almost unendurable by a multiplication of worldly misfortunes. An infection with smallpox when he was but four years old left his eyesight much impaired. In addition to his general lifelong weakness, he spent a joyless youth, his marriage was a constant source of unhappiness, his favorite child died of smallpox, his wife went mad and died, he was expelled from his lectureship at the University of Grätz when that city fell to the Catholics, his mother was charged and imprisoned for witchcraft and for almost a year he desperately tried to save her from the torture chamber, he himself very narrowly escaped condemnation of heterodoxy, and his stipend was always in arrears. One report says that his second marriage was even less fortunate than his first although he took the precaution to analyze carefully the merits and demerits of eleven girls before choosing the wrong one. He was forced to augment his income by casting horoscopes, and he died of a fever while on a journey to obtain some of his long overdue salary.

165° *Numerology and theology.*   It seems that in one respect numerology and theology are alike: it does not necessarily make any difference to a man's science what he believes or disbelieves about either. Some of the leading twentieth-century scientific numerologists are as distinguished in science as are their opponents who have only disrespect for all number mysticism.

GÉRARD DESARGUES AND BLAISE PASCAL

Gérard Desargues (1593–1662) and Blaise Pascal (1623–1662) were forerunners of the great nineteenth-century researchers in the field of projective geometry. Desargues was an engineer, architect, and one-time French army officer who, when he was in his thirties and living in Paris, made a considerable impression on his contemporaries through a series of gratuitous lectures on geometry that later led to a book. Among those who appreciated his work was the youthful Blaise Pascal, who was to become an eminent French mathematician, physicist, and man of letters. In fact, Pascal once credited Desargues as being the source of much of his inspiration. Desargues and Pascal died in the same year; Desargues was 69, but Pascal was only 39.

166° *Desargues' forgotten book.* In 1639, nine years after Kepler's death, there appeared in Paris a remarkably original but little heeded treatise on the conic sections, written by Gérard Desargues. The work was so generally neglected by other mathematicians that it was soon forgotten and all copies of the publication disappeared. Two centuries later, when the French geometer Michel Chasles wrote his history of geometry, there was no means of estimating the value of Desargues' work. Six years later, however, in 1845, Chasles happened upon a manuscript copy of the treatise, made by Desargues' pupil, Philippe de la Hire, and since that time the work has been recognized as a classic in the early development of synthetic projective geometry.

Several reasons can be advanced to account for the initial neglect of Desargues' little volume. It was overshadowed by the more supple analytic geometry introduced by Descartes two years earlier. Geometers were generally expending their energies either developing this new powerful tool or trying to apply infinitesimals to geometry. Also, Desargues adopted an unfortunate and eccentric style of writing. He introduced some seventy new terms, many of a recondite botanical origin, of which only one, *involution*, has survived, and, curiously enough, this one was preserved because it was the piece of Desargues' technical jargon that was singled out for the sharpest criticism and ridicule by his reviewer.

167° *The precocity of Pascal.* Pascal early showed unusual ability in mathematics, and several stories of his youthful accomplishments have been told by his sister Gilberta, who became Madame Périer. Because of a delicate constitution, the boy was kept at home to insure his not being overworked. His father decided that the youngster's education should be at first restricted to the study of languages and should not include any mathematics. The exclusion of mathematics from his studies aroused curiosity in the boy and he inquired of his tutor as to the nature of geometry. The tutor informed him that it was the study of exact figures and the properties of their different parts. Stimulated by his tutor's description of the subject and by his father's injunction against it, he gave up his playtime and clandestinely, in a few weeks, discovered for himself many properties of geometrical figures, in particular the fact that the sum of the angles of a triangle is equal to a straight angle. This latter was accomplished by some process of folding a paper triangle, perhaps by folding the vertices over to the center of the inscribed circle, as indicated in Figure 24, or by folding the vertices over to the foot of an altitude, as indicated in Figure 25. When

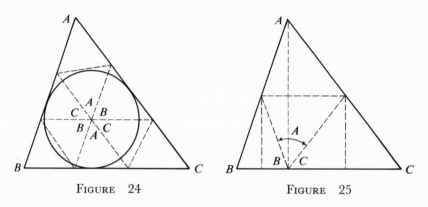

FIGURE 24   FIGURE 25

his father came upon him one day during his geometrical activities, he was so struck by the boy's ability that he gave his son a copy of Euclid's *Elements*, which the youngster read with avidity and quickly mastered.

At the age of fourteen, Pascal participated in the weekly gatherings of a group of French mathematicians from which the French Academy ultimately arose in 1666. When he was sixteen he wrote an essay on conic sections that Descartes could not believe was the work of the boy but thought it must be that of his father instead. At eighteen or nineteen he invented the first calculating machine, which he devised to assist his father in the auditing of government accounts at Rouen. Pascal was to manufacture over fifty calculating machines, some of which are still preserved in the Conservatoire des Arts et Métiers at Paris. At twenty-three he became interested in Torricelli's work on atmospheric pressure and began to apply his unusual talents to physics, with the result that *Pascal's principle* of hydrodynamics is today known to every student of high school physics.

168° *The greatest "might-have-been" in the history of mathematics.*
Pascal's astonishing and precocious activity came suddenly to an end
in 1650, when, suffering from frail health, he decided to abandon his
research in mathematics and science and to devote himself to religious
contemplation. Three years later, however, he returned briefly to
mathematics. At this time he wrote his *Traité du triangle arithmétique*
concerning a triangular arrangement of the binomial coefficients,
conducted several experiments on fluid pressure, and in correspondence
with Fermat assisted in laying the foundations of the mathematical
theory of probability. But late in 1654 he received what he regarded as
a strong intimation that these renewed activities were not pleasing to
God. The divine hint occurred when his runaway horses dashed over
the parapet of the bridge at Neuilly and he himself was saved only by
the miraculous breaking of the traces. Fortified with a reference to the
accident written on a small piece of parchment henceforth carried next
to his heart, he dutifully went back to his religious meditations.

Only once again, in 1658, did Pascal return to mathematics.
While suffering with toothache some geometrical ideas occurred to
him, and his teeth suddenly ceased to ache. Regarding this as a sign
of divine will, he obediently applied himself assiduously for eight days
toward developing his ideas, producing in this time a fairly full account
of the geometry of the cycloid curve and solving some problems that
subsequently, when issued as challenge problems, baffled other mathematicians. His famous *Provincial Letters* and his *Pensées*, which are read
today as models of early French literature, were written toward the
close of his brief life.

Pascal has been described as the greatest "might-have-been" in
the history of mathematics. With such unusual talents and such deep
geometrical intuition he should have produced, under more favorable
conditions, a great deal more. But his health was such that most of his
life was spent racked with physical pain, and from early manhood he
also suffered the mental torments of a religious neurotic.

169° *Pascal's "mystic hexagram" theorem.* The great gem of
Pascal's work on conic sections is the theorem, illustrated by Figure 26,
now known by his name: *The three points of intersection of the three pairs of
opposite sides of a (not necessarily convex) hexagon inscribed in a conic lie on a*

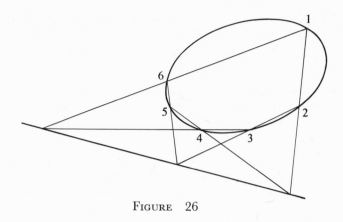

FIGURE   26

straight line. There is a report, quite likely a legend, that Pascal derived over four hundred corollaries to his great theorem, by considering special cases in which various of the vertices of the inscribed hexagon are allowed to coalesce. In any case, the consequences of Pascal's theorem are very numerous and attractive, and an almost unbelievable amount of research has been expended on the configuration. To illustrate, let us call the concerned line of collinearity the *Pascal line* of the given inscribed hexagon. There are $5!/2 = 60$ possible ways of forming a hexagon from six points on a conic, and, by Pascal's theorem, to each hexagon corresponds a Pascal line. These sixty Pascal lines pass three by three through twenty points, called *Steiner points*, which in turn lie four by four on fifteen lines, called *Plücker lines*. The Pascal lines also concur three by three in another set of points, called *Kirkman points*, of which there are sixty. Corresponding to each Steiner point, there are three Kirkman points such that all four lie upon a line, called a *Cayley line*. There are twenty of these Cayley lines, and they pass four by four through fifteen points, called *Salmon points*. There are many further extensions and properties of the configuration, and the number of different proofs that have been supplied for the "mystic hexagram" theorem itself is now legion.

170° *Lovis de Montalte and Amos Dettonville.* Pascal sometimes, as in his *Provincial Letters*, wrote under the nom de plume Lovis (Louis) de Montalte. In various of his challenge problems, he called himself Amos Dettonville, and this is why Leibniz occasionally refers to Pascal as Dettonville. The name Amos Dettonville is an anagram of the name Lovis de Montalte.

171° *Two very practical contributions.* It is interesting that Pascal has been credited with the invention of the one-wheeled wheelbarrow as we know it today. Also, at the age of thirty-five, he conceived the omnibus—an idea that was soon put into practice at five sous a ride.

172° *A specious use of probability.* In the seventh chapter of his *Pensées*, Pascal puts forth the argument that, since the value of eternal happiness must be infinite, then, even if the probability of a religious life ensuring happiness be very small, still the expectancy (which is measured by the product of the two) must be sufficient to render it worthwhile to be religious.

RENÉ DESCARTES AND PIERRE DE FERMAT

WHILE Desargues and Pascal were opening the new field of projective geometry, Descartes and Fermat were conceiving ideas of modern analytic geometry. There is a fundamental distinction between the two studies, for the former is a *branch* of geometry whereas the latter is a *method* of geometry. There are few academic experiences that can be more thrilling to the student of elementary mathematics than his introduction to this new and powerful method of attacking geometrical problems. The essence of the idea, as applied to the plane, is the establishment of a correspondence between ordered pairs of real numbers and points in the plane, thereby making possible a correspondence between curves in the plane and equations in two variables, so that for each curve in the plane there is an equation $f(x, y) = 0$, and for each such equation there is a curve, or set of points, in the plane. A correspondence is similarly established between the algebraic and analytic properties of the equation $f(x, y) = 0$ and the geometric properties of the associated curve. Geometry is cleverly reduced to algebra and analysis.

René Descartes was born near Tours in 1596. Shortly after he left school in 1612, he went to Paris and devoted some time to the study of mathematics. In 1617 he commenced several years of soldiering by first joining the army of Prince Maurice of Nassau. Upon quitting military life he spent four or five years traveling through Germany, Denmark, Holland, Switzerland, and Italy. After resettling for a couple of years in Paris, where he continued his mathematical studies and his philosophical contemplations, and where for a while he took up the construction of optical instruments, he decided to move to Holland, then at the height of its power. There he lived for twenty years, devoting his time to philosophy, mathematics, science, and writing. In 1649 he went to Stockholm, at the request of Queen Christina. He died there early in 1650.

Pierre de Fermat was born near Toulouse in 1601(?). He was the son of a leather merchant and received his early education at home. At the age of thirty he obtained the post of councillor for the local parliament at Toulouse and there discharged his duties with modesty and punctiliousness. Working as a humble and retiring lawyer, he devoted the bulk of his leisure time to the study of mathematics. Although he published very little during his lifetime, he was in scientific correspondence with many leading mathematicians of his day and in this way considerably influenced his contemporaries. He enriched so many branches of mathematics with so many important contributions that he has been called the greatest French mathematician of the seventeenth century. In particular, he is universally regarded as one of the very greatest number theorists of all times. He died in Castres in 1665.

173° *A challenge problem and a friendship.* There is a story, whose authenticity has been questioned, that after Descartes joined the army of Prince Maurice of Nassau in 1617, he was one day walking through the streets of Breda, where the army was stationed, when he came upon a posted placard in Dutch, which excited his curiosity. Stopping the first passerby, Descartes asked him to translate the placard into either French or Latin. The stranger, who happened to be Isaac Beeckman, the head of the Dutch College at Dort, agreed to do so provided Descartes would answer it, for the placard contained a challenge problem in geometry. Descartes solved the problem within a few hours and a warm friendship resulted between him and Beeckman.

174° *The birth of an idea.* There are a couple of legends describing the initial hint that led Descartes to the contemplation of analytic geometry. According to one story, it came to him in a dream. On St. Martin's Eve, November 10, 1619, while the army with which he was soldiering was lying inactive in its winter quarters on the banks of the Danube, Descartes experienced three singularly vivid and coherent dreams that, he claimed, changed the whole course of his life. The dreams, he said, clarified his purpose in life and determined his future endeavors by revealing to him "a marvelous science" and "a wonderful discovery." Descartes never explicitly disclosed just what were the marvelous science and the wonderful discovery, but some believe them to have been analytic geometry, or the application of algebra to geometry, and then the reduction of all the sciences to geometry. Eighteen years later he expounded some of his ideas in his famous philosophical treatise on universal science, *Discours de la méthode pour bien conduire sa raison et chercher la vérité dans les sciences* (Discourse on the Method of Correctly Guiding the Reason and Seeking Truth in the Sciences). This work was accompanied by three appendices illustrating the method; it was in the third of these that the world was given analytic geometry. The year of publication was 1637.

Another story, perhaps on a par with the story of Isaac Newton and the falling apple, says that the initial flash of analytic geometry came to Descartes when he was watching a fly crawl about on the ceiling near a corner of his room. It struck him that the path of the fly on the ceiling could be described if only one knew the relation connecting the fly's distances from the two adjacent walls. Even though this second story may be apocryphal, it has good pedagogical value.

175° *Descartes' advice.* As a youngster, Descartes suffered fragile health. When he was eight, he was sent to a Jesuit school at La Flèche. There Father Charlet, taking a personal interest in him and realizing that to educate the delicate boy's mind he must first build up his body, permitted the youngster to lie in bed in the mornings as late as he pleased and not to leave his room till he felt like joining his schoolmates. This pleasant custom developed into a lifelong habit. Descartes later averred that these meditative hours of morning rest constituted his most productive periods and were the source of his philosophy and mathematics.

When Descartes visited Pascal in 1647, he advised his sickly host to follow his example, to lie abed every morning till close to the noon hour and not to allow anyone to make him get up until he felt inclined to do so, claiming this to be the best way to do good work in mathematics and to preserve one's health. Unfortunately, Pascal did not heed his guest's excellent advice.

176° *Two significant contributions to mathematical notation.* In the third appendix, *La géométrie*, of his *Discours*, Descartes fixed the present-day custom of employing the first letters of the alphabet to denote known quantities and the last letters to denote unknown ones. He also introduced our present system of indices, such as a^3, a^4, and so forth. This system of indices had been suggested by earlier writers, but Descartes' adoption of the system, which was probably original on his part, fixed subsequent custom.

177° *The death of Descartes.* In 1649 Descartes received a pleading invitation from the nineteen-year-old Queen Christina of Sweden to bring learning to her court and to teach her philosophy. Dazzled by the aura of royalty and the man-of-war specially sent to fetch him, but yet with qualms and hesitation, Descartes finally exchanged his quiet and peaceful existence in Holland for a boisterous and hectic life in Stockholm. Queen Christina, who seems to have been much more of an athlete than a scholar, decided that five o'clock in the morning in a cold library with the windows thrown wide open was the only proper time and place to study philosophy. Accordingly, at some ungodly hour before the light of day, poor Descartes found himself roused from his warm bed and swept across a cold windy square to the chilly palace library to give the headstrong Queen her philosophy lessons. In addition to this madness, it was not very long before Descartes found himself the center of a veritable hornets' nest of malicious whisperings about foreign influence over the Queen. The cold unfriendly climate of Stockholm, the rupture of his deeply loved habit of lying abed until almost noon, and the destruction of his former quiet and private life were too much for him. After a few months in Sweden the weary philosopher fell ill with a fever accompanied by an inflammation of the lungs, dragged himself to a sick bed, and within ten days was dead, a victim of the conceited vanity of a willful girl.

178° *The Fermat numbers.* Some great men lead colorful personal lives that naturally give rise to fine stories and anecdotes, while others live such quiet, plodding, uneventful personal lives that nothing unusual is suggested. Pierre de Fermat belongs to the second category. And yet many stories can be told concerning Fermat, for though his personal life was indeed uneventful, his creative work in mathematics—or, in his case, we should say his recreation in mathematics—is full of interesting stories.

For example, Fermat died with the belief that he had found a long-sought-for prime-yielding expression in the formula

$$F_n = 2^{2^n} + 1.$$

In no less than seven different places did he express his conviction that F_n is a prime number for all nonnegative integral values of n, though he was always careful to admit that he had no proof of the conjecture. For $n = 0, 1, 2, 3, 4$ we have $F_n = 3, 5, 17, 257, 65{,}537$, respectively, and these are all prime numbers. But, in 1732, the great Swiss mathematician Leonhard Euler showed that

$$F_5 = 4{,}294{,}967{,}297 = (6{,}700{,}417)(641),$$

and thus is composite. Since then, by clever individual proofs not capable of any general application, F_n has also been shown to be composite for $n = 6, 7, 8, 9, 11, 12, 15, 18, 23, 36, 38, 73$, and in no other case than for $n = 0, 1, 2, 3, 4$ has F_n been shown to be prime. The result is that, whereas Fermat felt that F_n is prime for all nonnegative integral n, the general feeling among mathematicians today is that, except for $n = 0, 1, 2, 3,$ and 4, F_n is always composite.

The numbers F_n are known as *Fermat numbers*, and they increase rapidly in size with increasing n. For example F_{10}, the first case whose primality or nonprimality is not yet determined, contains 309 digits.

The number F_{36} has been shown to contain more than twenty trillion digits. And the number F_{73} has been shown to be so large that if it were written out in digits of type of the size in this book, all the books in all the libraries of the world would not suffice to record it!

A very remarkable discovery was made in 1796 in connection with the Fermat numbers. The ancient Greeks had shown how, with straightedge and compasses, regular polygons of three, four, five, six, and fifteen sides can be constructed. By successive angle, or arc, bisections, we may then with Euclidean tools construct regular polygons having 2^n, $3(2^n)$, $5(2^n)$, and $15(2^n)$ sides. Not until almost the nineteenth century was it known that any other regular polygons can be constructed with these limited tools. In 1796, the eminent German mathematician Carl Friedrich Gauss, when only nineteen years old, developed the theory that shows that a regular polygon having a *prime* number of sides can be constructed with Euclidean tools if and only if that number is a prime Fermat number. Thus, unknown to the Greeks, regular polygons of 17, 257, and 65,537 sides can be constructed with straightedge and compasses.

Many Euclidean constructions of the regular polygon of seventeen sides have been given. In 1832, Richelot published an investigation of the regular polygon of 257 sides, and a Professor Hermes of Lingen gave up ten years of his life to the problem of constructing a regular polygon of 65,537 sides. It has been said that it was Gauss's youthful discovery that a regular polygon of seventeen sides can be constructed with straightedge and compasses that made him decide to devote his life to mathematics. His pride in this discovery is evidenced by his request that a regular polygon of seventeen sides be engraved on his tombstone. Although this request was never fulfilled, such a polygon is found on the base of a monument to Gauss erected at his birthplace in Brunswick.

179° *Fermat's method of infinite descent.* [The following is adapted, with permission, from the article by Howard Eves, of the same title, that appeared in the Historically Speaking section of *The Mathematics Teacher*, March, 1960, pp. 195–196.]

Diophantus, the famous Greek number theorist of antiquity, wrote at least three mathematical works, of which his *Arithmetica* is by far the most important. The *Arithmetica* is an analytical treatment of algebraic number theory that marks the author as a genius in this field. Only six of the original thirteen books of the *Arithmetica* are extant, and these six books are devoted to the solution of about 130 number problems of considerable variety and degree of difficulty. There have been many commentaries of the *Arithmetica*, but it was Regiomontanus who, in 1463, called for a Latin translation of the extant Greek text. The call was met in 1575 by Xylander (the Greek name assumed by Wilhelm Holzmann, a professor of mathematics at the University of Heidelberg), who made a meritorious translation with commentary. This Xylander translation was later used by the Frenchman Bachet de Méziriac when, in 1621, he published the first edition of the Greek text along with a Latin translation and notes.

Pierre de Fermat secured a copy of the Bachet edition of Diophantus's *Arithmetica* and used the copy as a combination textbook and notebook. Many of Fermat's contributions to the field of number theory occur as marginal statements inserted in his copy of the *Arithmetica*. In 1670, five years after Fermat's death, these marginal notes were incorporated in a new, but unfortunately carelessly printed, edition of the *Arithmetica*, brought out by Fermat's son, Clément-Samuel. In this edition we find, accompanying Problem 26 of Book VI, the following marginal note by Fermat.

> The area of a right triangle whose sides are rational numbers cannot be a square number. I have obtained a proof of this theorem only after extensive and arduous effort. I here reproduce the proof, since the procedure used will make possible wonderful progress in number theory.

Then follows an indication of the proof.

The procedure alluded to by Fermat is ingenious, and has since become known as *Fermat's method of infinite descent*. The method apparently was used with success by Fermat on a number of occasions. For example, in one of his letters to Roberval, Fermat describes the difficulties he experienced in trying to establish a celebrated conjecture made by Bachet that every positive integer can be written as the sum of at most four squares, and in the letter Fermat says that he finally succeeded by the use of his favorite method of infinite descent. Again, in 1897 a paper was found in the library at Leyden among the manuscripts of Christiaan Huygens, in which Fermat describes the method of infinite descent.

The method of infinite descent is particularly useful in establishing negative results. In outline the method is this. To prove that there do not exist positive integers $a, b, c, \ldots$ satisfying a relation $R(a, b, c, \ldots)$, assume the contrary. On this assumption show that $R(a_1, b_1, c_1, \ldots)$ holds, where a_1 is a positive integer and $a_1 < a$. Then in like manner we may show that $R(a_2, b_2, c_2, \ldots)$ holds, where a_2 is a positive integer and $a_2 < a_1$, and so on ad infinitum. But, since there are only a finite number of positive integers less than a, this is impossible. We are thus led to a contradiction, whence we conclude that the relation $R(a, b, c, \ldots)$ is not satisfied by positive integers $a, b, c, \ldots$.

To clarify the Fermat method of infinite descent, let us consider a simple application of the method. Let us prove by the method that $\sqrt{2}$ is irrational. Suppose, on the contrary, that $\sqrt{2} = a/b$, where a and b are positive integers. Now

$$\sqrt{2} + 1 = 1/(\sqrt{2} - 1),$$

whence

$$\frac{a}{b} + 1 = \frac{1}{\dfrac{a}{b} - 1} = \frac{b}{a - b},$$

and

$$\sqrt{2} = \frac{a}{b} = \frac{b}{a - b} - 1 = \frac{2b - a}{a - b} = \frac{a_1}{b_1}, \text{ say.}$$

But, since $1 < \sqrt{2} < 2$, after replacing $\sqrt{2}$ by a/b and then multiplying through by b, we have $b < a < 2b$. Now, since $a < 2b$, it follows that $0 < 2b - a = a_1$. And since $b < a$, it follows that $a_1 = 2b - a < a$. Thus a_1 is a positive integer less than a. By a reapplication of our procedure we find $\sqrt{2} = a_2/b_2$, where a_2 is a positive integer less than a_1. The process may be repeated indefinitely. But the positive integers cannot be decreased in magnitude indefinitely. It therefore follows that our original assumption that $\sqrt{2} = a/b$, where a and b are positive integers, is untenable. That is, $\sqrt{2}$ is irrational.

180° *The most tantalizing marginal note in the history of mathematics.* Of the well over three thousand mathematical papers and notes that he wrote, Fermat published only one, and that just five years before his death and under the concealing initials M. P. E. A. S. Many of his mathematical findings were disclosed in letters to fellow mathematicians and in marginal notes inserted in his copy of Bachet's translation of Diophantus's *Arithmetica*.

At the side of Problem 8 of Book II in his copy of Diophantus, Fermat wrote what has become the most tantalizing marginal note in the history of mathematics. The considered problem in Diophantus is: "To divide a given square number into two squares." Fermat's accompanying marginal note reads:

> To divide a cube into two cubes, a fourth power, or in general any power whatever above the second, into two powers of the same denomination, is impossible, and I have assuredly found an admirable proof of this, but the margin is too narrow to contain it.

This famous conjecture, which says that *there do not exist positive integers x, y, z, n such that $x^n + y^n = z^n$ when n > 2*, has become known as "Fermat's last theorem." Whether Fermat really possessed a sound demonstration of this conjecture will probably forever remain an enigma. Because of his unquestionable integrity we must accept as a fact that he thought he had a proof, and because of his paramount ability we must accept as a fact that if the proof contained a fallacy then that fallacy must have been very subtle.

Many of the most prominent mathematicians since Fermat's time have tried their skill on the problem, but the general conjecture still remains open. There is a proof given elsewhere by Fermat for the case $n = 4$, and Euler supplied a proof (later perfected by others) for $n = 3$. About 1825, independent proofs for the case $n = 5$ were given by Legendre and Dirichlet, and in 1839 Lamé proved the conjecture for $n = 7$. Very significant advances in the study of the problem were made by the German mathematician E. Kummer. In 1843, Kummer submitted a purported proof of the general conjecture to Dirichlet, who pointed out an error in the reasoning. Kummer then returned to the problem with renewed vigor, and a few years later, after developing an important allied subject in higher algebra called the *theory of ideals*, derived very general conditions for the insolvability of the Fermat relation. Almost all important subsequent progress on the problem has been based on Kummer's investigations. It is now known that "Fermat's last theorem" is certainly true for all $n < 4003$ (this was shown in 1955, with the aid of the SWAC digital computer), and for many other special values of n.

In 1908, the German mathematician P. Wolfskehl bequeathed 100,000 marks to the Academy of Science at Göttingen as a prize for the first complete proof of the "theorem." The result was a deluge of alleged proofs by glory-seeking and money-seeking laymen, and, ever since, the problem has haunted amateurs somewhat as does the trisection of an arbitrary angle and the squaring of the circle. "Fermat's last theorem" has the peculiar distinction of being the mathematical problem for which the greatest number of incorrect proofs have been published.